BASIC PRINCIPLES OF
SENSORY EVALUATION

Sponsored by
Committee E-18 on
Sensory Evaluation of Materials and Products
AMERICAN SOCIETY FOR
TESTING AND MATERIALS

ASTM SPECIAL TECHNICAL PUBLICATION NO. 433

List price $5.75; 30 per cent discount to members

published by the
AMERICAN SOCIETY FOR TESTING AND MATERIALS
1916 Race Street, Philadelphia, Pa. 19103

NOTE

The Society is not responsible, as a body,
for the statements and opinions
advanced in this publication.

Printed in Baltimore, Md.
May, 1968
April 1969
April 1973

Foreword

This special technical publication on Basic Principles of Sensory Evaluation was sponsored by Subcommittee II on Principles of Psychophysical Test Methods of Committee E-18 on Sensory Evaluation of Materials and Products. The papers were compiled by members of Subcommittee II with W. H. Danker, Fritzsche Brothers, Inc., serving as chairman.

Related
ASTM Publications

Manual on Sensory Testing Methods, STP 434 (1968),
$4.25

Correlation of Subjective-Objective Methods in the
Study of Odors and Taste, STP 440 (1968),
$5.75

Contents

Historical Background for ASTM Committee E-18

The American Society for Testing and Materials (ASTM) is an international, nonprofit, technical, scientific, and educational body for "the promotion of knowledge of materials of engineering and the standardization of specifications and methods of testing." ASTM provides a forum for persons of diverse experience and academic background and representing a variety of affiliations. Through the Technical Committees of the Society, those people may join together to promote advances in the science of measurement for their respective fields. These advances may be in the form of analytical standards, specifications, or symposia on selected subjects. No other technical organization in North America is historically or organizationally sufficiently flexible to provide such an opportunity. It was natural, therefore, that individuals concerned with sensory evaluation should find a common meeting ground in ASTM.

In 1945, ASTM appointed an Administrative Committee on Ultimate Consumer Goods to consider what might be done within the Society regarding engineering test methods for consumer goods. Interest in this area had developed primarily in the work of Committee D-13 on Textiles, which had several subcommittees assigned to problems that concerned individual rather than institutional users.

The new Administrative Committee appointed two subcommittees, one in the natural science and the other in the social science field. It became apparent that the social science approach, without engineering or economic considerations, was insufficient to determine quality control limits and to specify test methods for materials and products that are designed for ultimate users. When these two subcommittees were discharged, it was decided to appoint a joint committee to bring together the natural and social science viewpoints. The first result was a Symposium on the Measurement of Consumer Wants held at the ASTM Annual Meeting at Atlantic City in 1951. The papers presented at this meeting appeared in 1952 as *ASTM STP 117.*

In September 1957, Rutgers University held a Conference on Quality Control and the Consumer, bringing together engineers and others from government, industry, and consumer services. At this meeting the work that ASTM had done in this field was reviewed. The papers presented at this Conference were published by Rutgers University.

The Administrative Committee, renamed the Administrative Committee on End-Use Products, was discharged after its last meeting on 3

December 1958. Its final recommendation was that ASTM set up a permanent committee to develop standards in the area of preference testing, psychophysical aspects, and other matters where human factors play a part in tests on materials.

The recommendation was developed by the Society in 1959, and an organization meeting was held on 14 January 1960. A steering committee was organized, and, at their first meeting on 29 April 1960, officers were appointed and a scope of activities defined. The new Committee was designated E-18 on Sensory Evaluation of Materials and Products.

Scope

A statement of scope as extracted from the Committee E-18 Bylaws is as follows:

The promotion of knowledge, stimulation of research, and the development of principles and recommended practices for the sensory evaluation (including discrimination and preference) of materials and products. These aims shall be furthered by:
1. Cooperation with other committees of the Society and with other organizations.
2. Preparation of standard definitions and nomenclature.
3. Establishment of principles of psychophysical test methods.
4. Preparation of recommended practices for design and conduct of tests, collection of data, and analysis and interpretation of results.
5. Fostering study of relationships between sensory evaluations and physical and chemical measurements.
6. Dissemination of information by technical publications and symposia.

Subcommittee I, Definitions and Nomenclature, is standardizing definitions of terms used in sensory evaluation. Definitions in existing compilations have been carefully considered, such as those issued by the Institute of Food Technologists; Amerine, Pangborn, and Roessler's *Principles of Sensory Evaluation of Food;* and others. The best possible compromise has been achieved in developing new definitions so that the result will not be just another list.

Subcommittee II, Principles of Psychophysical Test Methods, has compiled a critical and exhaustive dissertation on its subject which follows herein as ASTM STP 433. The resulting text should be of considerable value to those active in the field. Originally it has been proposed that analytical procedures be developed for various applications and issued as standards. However, the very nature of sensory testing and the diversity of possible applications dictated that a basis of common communication outside and within the committee be established. Production of STP's to serve as basic references was deemed the wisest first step.

Subcommittee III, Preparation of Recommended Practices, has also compiled an intensive examination of its subject particularly on odor and taste. ASTM STP 434, *Manual on Sensory Testing Methods,* is a companion book to this one sponsored by Subcommittee II. As in ASTM STP 433 references have been produced of value for both the novice and experienced practitioner in the sensory field.

Subcommittee IV, Instrumental-Sensory Correlation, has as its major objective to ultimately recommend practices for the correlation of instrumental and sensory methods of analysis. The initial step in this admittedly long range objective is to critically review the existing literature, to select those publications that have degrees, hopefully high, of correlation. To this end 20 members of this subcommittee have been assigned specific journals for comprehensive coverage.

Subcommittee IV also decided to start its activities with the senses of odor and taste. It has sponsored a symposium on the Correlation of Subjective-Objective Methods in the Study of Odors and Taste at the 70th Annual Meeting of ASTM held in Boston, Mass., on 28 June 1967. The papers in that symposium are being published as ASTM STP 440 in conjunction with ASTM STP 433 and ASTM STP 434.

Fields of interest currently represented in the committee include: air pollution, clothing and textiles, metals and appliances, beverages and liquors, manufactured food products, flavors and fragrances, agricultural commodities, naval stores, tobacco, chemicals, paints and varnishes, paper and plastics, telephone, railroads, petroleum and allied products, laboratory equipment, packaging materials, and pharmaceuticals.

Some of the disciplines of committee members brought to bear on the subject of sensory evaluation are: psychometry, psychology, statistics, chemistry, food technology, engineering, marketing, metallurgy, biology, and physiology.

Some areas being considered for the future are: design and interpretation of experiments, texture (other than food), appearance, consumer tests, instrument-sensory correlation, sequence used for product testing (from laboratory to field test), panel costs, marketing, and computer use in sensory evaluations.

Suggestions are welcomed for other areas to be treated in the future.

Acknowledgments

Appreciation is due the following for their major contributions in the preparation of the history and purpose of this special technical publication: R. A. Baker, J. P. Duncanson, P. S. Olmstead, W. H. Stahl, Amos Turk.

W. H. Danker
Chairman, Subcommittee II of Committee E-18.

Introduction

This publication contains articles by members of Subcommittee II on Principles of Psychophysical Test Methods of ASTM, Committee E-18 on Sensory Evaluation of Materials and Products, and by other experts in the various fields. It covers major areas basic to sensory evaluation, brief physiological background, and an outline of some principles underlying methods of sensory evaluation. A comprehensive compilation of such methodology has been prepared by Subcommittee III on Preparation of Recommended Practices of Committee E-18 under the title *Manual on Sensory Testing Methods," ASTM STP 434.*

W. H. Danker
Chairman, Subcommittee II of Committee E-18

PART I: The Nature of Stimuli

Dean Foster[1] and W. H. Danker[2]

The Nature of Stimuli

REFERENCE: Foster, Dean and Danker, W. H., **"The Nature of Stimuli,"** *Basic Principles of Sensory Evaluation, ASTM STP 433,* American Society for Testing and Materials, 1968, pp. 7–10.

Since our primary objective is to aid ASTM, a review was made of the materials evaluated by ASTM. It was found that these materials could be roughly classified into ten major groups (Table 1). Then the characteristics of these materials were grouped as stimuli opposite the receptor they affect (Table 2).

A stimulus, for the purpose of this publication, is defined as any chemical or physical activator which causes a response in a receptor. For example, the eye is the receptor for light stimuli, the ear for sound stimuli. The receptor for each of our senses is specialized to receive only one class of stimuli. Nerve impulses then travel from receptors to the brain for interpretation into sensations.

Only six classes of stimuli exist: (1) mechanical, (2) thermal, (3) photic, (4) acoustic, (5) chemical, and (6) electrical[3] (see Table 3). An effective stimulus produces a sensation, the dimensions of which are: quality, intensity, extension, duration, and like and dislike. The stimuli in all six classes are measured by physical or chemical methods, the sensation by psychological procedures.

The least energy capable of producing a sensation is called an *absolute threshold.* As the stimulus energy is increased, sensation changes in lawful ways which are slightly different for each sense. The least stimulus change perceptible is termed a *difference threshold.* Both absolute and difference thresholds are important concepts for gaging the relation between stimulus and sensation, a psycho-physical relation.

Man possesses many different senses, perhaps 30 or 40 in all, depending upon the means of classification. For present purposes we are concerned only with sight or vision, hearing, smell, taste, and the four cutaneous (skin) senses: cold, warmth, pressure, and pain.

[1] Virginia Military Institute, Lexington, Va.
[2] Fritzsche Brothers, Inc., New York, N. Y.
[3] Geldard, F. A., *Introduction to Psychology,* Wiley, New York, 1962.

7

TABLE 1—*Some products evaluated by ASTM.*

1. *Adhesives:*
   Cements
   Glues
   Tackings

2. *Cleansers:*
   Detergents
   Polishes
   Waxes

3. *Coverings:*
   Inks
   Lacquers
   Paints
   Varnishes

4. *Hydrocarbons:*
   Fuels
   Greases
   Hydraulics
   Oils
   Waxes

5. *Insulators:*
   Acoustical
   Electrical
   Heating

6. *Minerals:*
   Bitumins
   Gypsums
   Concrete

7. *Plastics:*
   Films
   Rubbers
   Vinyls

8. *Textiles:*
   Cloth
   Fiber
   Leather
   Plastic

9. *Water and beverages*

10. *Airborne materials:*
    Aerosols
    Exhausts
    Pollutants
    Smoke

TABLE 2—*Some ASTM product "stimuli" and their "receptors."*

Stimuli to be measured	Receptors
I. Appearance	eyes
(a) Color	
(b) Grayness	
(c) Intensity	
(d) Surface	
1. Pattern	
2. Grain	
3. Sheen	
4. Uniformity	
II. Feel	touch
(a) Drape	
(b) Elasticity	
(c) Grain	
(d) Hand	
(e) Hardness	
(f) Nap	
(g) Plasticity	
(h) Stickiness	
(i) Viscosity	
III. Odor	nose
IV. Sound	ear
V. Taste	taste buds
VI. Temperature	heat, cold receptors

TABLE 3—*Classification of the senses.*[a]

Modality	Sense Organ	Peripheral Nerve Endings	Cortical Nerve Projections	Normal Stimulus	Sensory Qualities
Vision	eye	rods and cones of retina	occipital lobe	photic energy	colors (red, gray)
Audition	ear	hair cells of organ of Corti	temporal lobe	acoustic energy	tones and noises
Cutaneous sensitivity	skin	specialized and free nerve endings	parietal lobe	mechanical and thermal energy	pressure pain, heat, cold
Olfaction	olfactory cleft of nostril	rods of olfactory epithelium	rhinencephalon	volatile substances	odors (fragrant, spicy)
Gustation	tongue and mouth region	taste buds of papillae	parietal lobe	soluble substances	sweet, salt, sour, bitter
Kinesthesis	muscles joints, tendons	specialized and free nerve endings	parietal lobe	mechanical energy	pressure, pain
Labyrinthine sensitivity	nonauditory labyrinth	hair cells of crista and macula	none (?); projects to the cerebellum	mechanical forces and gravity	none
Organic sensitivity	portions of gastro-intestinal tract	specialized and free nerve endings	parietal lobe	mechanical energy	pain, pressure

[a] See footnote 3.

For assaying the dimension of a response or sensation several different methods may be utilized. They are magnitude estimation, ratio estimation, method of limits, average error. These methods are listed and explained in the Committee E-18 *Manual on Sensory Testing Methods.*[4]

For background in sensory evaluations we will briefly review receptor anatomy and the nerve connections with parts of the brain. The range of physical and chemical activators which are stimuli will be discussed. Examples of how the receptors respond and adapt to the stimuli will be outlined.

[4] Committee E-18, *Manual on Sensory Testing Methods, ASTM STP 434* American Society for Testing and Materials, 1968.

PART II: The Senses—Physiological Background

B. P. McNamara[1] and W. H. Danker[2]

Odor and Taste

REFERENCE: McNamara, B. P. and Danker, W. H., **"Odor and Taste,"** *Basic Principles of Sensory Evaluation, ASTM STP 433,* American Society for Testing and Materials, 1968, pp. 13–18.

Odor

Odor stimuli affect only a small area of yellow brown receptor cells located in the ceiling of the inner nose. This area contains millions of nerve endings of the olfactory nerves [1].[3] Each nerve ending, in turn, has at its tip several fine cilia-like hairs, which are thought to contain the ultimate olfactory receptors [2]. These hairs protrude into the mucous layer which is continuous with that lining the entire surface of the inner nose. The olfactory nerves transmit impulses to the olfactory bulb located at the front and the base of the brain. At the bulb, fibers from the nose contact other nerves which go to different parts of the brain (see Fig. 1).

Much of the brain has been tapped with fine electrodes to examine the path of impulses from odor stimuli.

In odor evaluations it is necessary that a substance is volatile enough to get into the air near the sensory area. The substance must be at least partly soluble in the mucous covering the olfactory receptors. Finally a minimum number of odorous particles must be in contact with the receptors for a minimum length of time.

To ensure adequate contact of odors with sensory cells, some panel leaders recommend that the judges take quick sniffs to get the odors high up into the nose. Gentle sniffs may result in the deflection of the odorous air stream by the lower ledges of the nose [3]. If a judge has a cold, his nostrils may be blocked by the swelling of the lining of the nose.

Most people can perceive a great many different odors. Some flavor experts can identify thousands of odors.

[1] Chief, Toxicology Dept., Medical Research Laboratory, Research Laboratories, Edgewood Arsenal, Md.

[2] Fritzsche Brothers, Inc., New York, N. Y.

[3] The italic numbers in brackets refer to the list of references appended to this paper.

Some odors can mask others to some extent or even entirely.

Some compounds within a similar odor class cannot be detected after one has been smelling another odor of that class. A second sample of the same odorous material cannot be detected if one has been exposed to the odor of the first sample too long. A judge after losing sensitivity to one odor in a mixture may better be able to evaluate the other odors in the mixture.

Response to odors as recorded electrically is very rapid. For most sub-

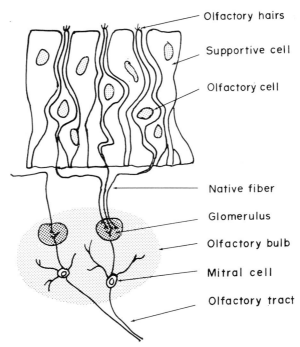

FIG. 1—*Schematic drawing of the olfactory membrane and odor-sensitive structures.*

stances recovery of sensitivity to its odor is also very rapid if clean air is breathed for a few seconds between evaluations. If interest is maintained, more than 70 odors can be evaluated in an hour [4].

Odorous materials vary considerably in strength. For some very strong odors one needs only 1/1,000,000 the concentration in air for detection than the concentration needed for weak odors [5].

Many theories have been proposed for the explanation of the mechanism for smelling odors [6]. None has proven to be complete or entirely correct to date. The theories proposing that there are absorption sites on the olfactory hairs for different odors, and that temporal and spatial patterns of neural activity are responsible for the sensing of different odors, have received more acceptance in recent years than have the other theories. It is thought probable that some enzymatic changes occur in the receptor during smelling.

Taste (Chemical Sense)

The receptors for taste are taste buds, most of which are located on the tongue. However, regions responsive to taste are also found on the palate, in the pharynx and larynx, on the tonsils and epiglottis, and, in some people at least, on the mucosa of the lips and cheeks, the underside of the tongue, and in the floor of the mouth. The areas of greatest responsiveness, however, are on the upper surface of the tongue, at its tip, sides, and rear surfaces. There is an area in the middle of the tongue which has no taste receptors. The receptors or taste buds (Fig. 2) are composed of a group of from two to twelve taste cells in a cluster with

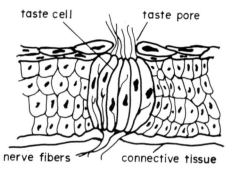

FIG. 2—*Schematic representation of a taste bud.*

supporting cells. The taste cells are arranged like the staves of a barrel. On the tip of each cell are cilia which extend into a pore in the skin which opens to the surface of the mouth. Protuberences of skin or papilla contain the taste buds. Four forms of papilla are found in the mouth: fungiform, foliate, circumvalate, and filiform. All but the filiform contain taste buds. There are on the average over 9000 taste buds in the mouth [7], most are in the several hundred circumvalate papilla. Beidler has observed that taste cells constantly degenerate and regenerate. Their half life is surprisingly short—about eight days. In old age some of the taste buds atrophy [8].

Nerve fibers from the taste buds (Fig. 2) carry messages as electric impulses to the brain. Studies have been made of these impulses on their path to the brain. Individual fibers from taste buds may carry impulses from one or more taste buds. These fibers join one of three major nerve bundles to the brain—cranial nerves VII, IX, and X; the facial; the glossopharyngeal; and the vagus. These nerves have connections with the thalamic portion of the brain which in turn has nerve connections with the cerebral cortex. These nerve connections and those they hook up with are the anatomical bases for our sense of taste. Only part of the interconnections are known.

Four major tastes exist:

1. *Sourness*—This is the simplest taste. It has as activators only acids, specifically hydrogen ions. Uusually the more hydrogen ions, the more sour the solution. However buffers in a sour solution may appreciably alter the hydrogen concentration and therefore the sour taste of the sample.

2. *Sweetness*—The most common sweetness activators are sugars. Many compounds of quite different chemical composition, however, have a sweet taste—some lead salts, saccharine, cyclamates, *d*-asparagine, for example.

3. *Saltiness*—Sodium chloride (table salt) has the most pure salty taste and is unique in this respect since most soluble inorganic compounds have several tastes such as bitter, alkaline, sweet, and salt in various combinations.

Taste strength of common chemical salts varies with either part of the molecule. The generally accepted order of cation strength is $NH_4 > K > Ca > Na > Li > Mg$. Rank order for anions of sodium is $SO_4 > Cl > Br > I > HCO_3 > NO_3$; Mg, NO_3 being the weakest.

4. *Bitterness*—Many chemically different compounds have a bitter taste. Some of the most bitter are alkaloids like caffeine, nicotine, quinine, and brucine.

Adaptation and Fatigue

Adaptation and fatigue to the four major tastes vary considerably.

Saltiness—Among 24 different inorganic salts, adaptation for one did not affect the sensitivity to others.

Sourness—Adaptation for one acid reduces a taster's sensitivity for any other acids since only the H+ is the sourness activator. Recovery of sensitivity is rapid since the most common acids are quite soluble and are readily rinsed away with normal salivation. The speed of stimulation and its duration can be considerably modified by buffers present in saliva or present in the mouth at the same time.

Sweetness—Adaptation to one sweetening agent may or may not reduce sensitivity to another. Sugar and saccharine do not fatigue sensitivity one for the other. Recovery of sensitivity for some of the sugars is more rapid than that for other sweeteners.

Bitterness—This taste may be quite lasting, more so than for the other basic tastes. One reason for this may be that many bitter substances have an appreciable affinity for the skin [9] and probably for its taste buds. The bitterness may last for over 1 min even after rinsing.

Thresholds—There is a large variation among the four basic tastes in the concentration needed to activate the receptors. Threshold concentration for sugar is greater than that for salt, greater for salt than for sour, and still less of many bitter substances can be tasted.

In general, much higher concentrations are needed to detect tastes than to detect odors.

Individuals vary greatly as to the minimum concentration which is barely detectable. Most sensitive tasters can detect as little as $\frac{1}{50}$ the concentration of a substance as can less sensitive tasters [10]. The determination of this concentration or threshold level varies greatly with the method used. Literature values vary greatly, and therefore the method used must be clearly understood when using reported values. Much variation for any individual may occur during the day and from day to day.

The relation of the temperature of a solution to be tasted and taste sensitivity differs for various substances [11]. Salt threshold increases from 17 to 42 C at a steady rate. A sweetener (Dulcin) threshold decreases from 17 to 35 C then increases slightly to 42 C. Quinine threshold increases slightly from 17 to 37 C and then increases rapidly to 42 C. Sourness thresholds remain about the same through the 17 to 42 C range.

On the tongue some areas are more sensitive to one taste than to another. Bitter solutions are better tasted at the back of the tongue and sweetness at the tip. Sensiiviy to salt is about the same on most tongue areas. Acids can best be detected along the sides of the tongue from midway to the back.

Many salts have several tastes. Epsom salt is bitter at the back and salty near the front of the tongue. Sodium bicarbonate is salty and bitter. Some substances like phenylthiourea have a taste to only part of the population [12]. This compound has a very large variation in threshold for detection for different people. In some geographical areas all people can detect its bitterness at low levels—in most areas only three of four persons can taste its bitterness. The taste of this compound is also called salty, or sweet, or sour by some people. It has been shown that this geographic variation has an inherited factor.

In conclusion, odor and taste are senses which are not so fully understood as are the senses of hearing or seeing. They are therefore more difficult to evaluate. This lack of understanding, however, is a major reason for the existence of our E-18 committee. That is why we were forced to develop these special sensory evaluation techniques. They are necessary since accurate physico-chemical instruments have not been available for odor and taste as they are for hearing and seeing. In recent years, highly sophisticated instruments and chromatographic techniques have been developed which promise to make future evaluations of odor and taste more accurate.

References

[1] Moulton, D. J. and Tucker, D., "Electrophysiology of Olfactory System, Recent Advances in Odor," *Annals of New York Academy of Sciences,* Vol. 116, Art. 2, New York, 1964, pp. 380–428.

[2] de Lorenzo, A. J. D., *Olfaction and Taste,* Zotterman, Y., ed., Macmillan, New York, 1963, pp. 5–10.

[3] De Vries, H. and Stuiver, M., *Sensory Communications,* Rosenblith, W. A., ed., Vol. 1, New York, p. 163.

[4] Pfaffman, C., *Symposium on Food Acceptance Testing Methodology,* Quartermaster Food and Container Institute, Oct. 1954, p. 6.

[5] Moncrieff, R. W., *Chemical Senses,* Wiley, New York, p. 80.

[6] Amerine, M. A., Pangborn, R. M., and Roessler, E. B., *Principles of Sensory Evaluation of Food,* Academic Press, New York, 1965, pp. 193–206.

[7] Cole, E. C., *Comparative Histology,* Blackiston, Philadelphia, 1941.

[8] Beidler, L. M., "Taste Receptor Stimulation," *Biophysical Chemistry,* Vol. 12, 1964, pp. 107–151.

[9] Wells, F. V., "Duration of Odorants on Skin," *Soap, Perfumery and Cosmetics Year Book,* United Trade Press, London, 1966, pp. 107–110.

[10] Blakeslee, A. F. and Salmon, T. H., "Genetics of Sensory Thresholds," *Proceedings of the National Academy of Sciences,* Washington, 1935, pp. 84–90.

[11] Hahn, H., *Klinische Wochenschrift,* Vol. 15, 1936, p. 15.

[12] Harris, H., *Introduction to Human Biochemical Genetics,* Cambridge, London, 1955.

B. P. McNamara[1]

Vision

REFERENCE: McNamara, B. P., **Vision,** *Basic Principles of Sensory Evaluation, ASTM STP 433,* American Society for Testing and Materials, 1968, pp. 19–23.

Vision is a complex phenomenon consisting of several basic components. Sight from external sources is brought to a focus on the retina of the eye. Changes are produced which initiate electrical impulses. These are conducted over the optic nerve and optic tract to the brain where the visual sensation is perceived and interpreted.

The Eye

The orb of the eye is composed of three layers as shown in Fig. 1. The outer protective layer is sclera containing the anterior portion of the transparent cornea. The middle layer of the vascular choroid is modified anteriorly into the ciliary body and the iris. The posterior two thirds of the inner layer is the retina containing the rods and cones which are the neural receptors of light. The inner layer extends over the ciliary body as the ciliary epithelium. In the center of the retina is located the fovea centralis. This area, containing only cones, is the site of greatest visual acuity. The anterior chamber is filled with clear fluid aqueous humor. The lens is a transparent convex body whose curvature can be altered by the ciliary muscles to focus onto the retina the images of external objects. In front of the lens is the iris, a thin muscular diaphragm with a center opening, the pupil. The diameter of the pupil alters to regulate the amount of light entering the eye.

The lens is devoid of blood vessels and receives its nourishment from the aqueous and vitreous fluids which bathe its surfaces. The lens capsule is a semipermeable membrane separating an area of high osmotic pressure within the lens from the area of lower osmotic pressure of the aqueous fluid. During accommodation fluid presumably passes into the lens. When the ciliary muscle is relaxed the pressure within the lens is increased and fluids are expelled.

[1] Chief, Texicology Dept., Medical Research Laboratory, Research Laboratories, Edgewood Arsenal, Md.

The cornea receives its oxygen from the air, the aqueous humor, and the limbus by slow diffusion. When oxygen consumption is inhibited by cyanide the vegetative activity seems to continue by aerobic glycolysis.

Eye Movements

The movements of the two eyes must be coordinated so that light from an object falls upon the two fovea, thus producing fusion into a single image. The movements are controlled by six extrinsic muscles which are attached to the eyeballs. The various muscles are innervated by three cranial nerves whose interactions are coordinated in the cerebral cortex.

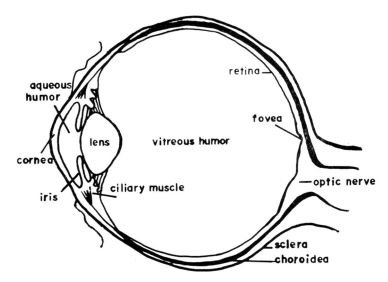

FIG. 1—*Schematic drawing of the eye.*

Accommodation

Accommodation is the alteration in the shape of the lens in effort to focus near or far images on the retina. The lens is held in an elongated shape by the suspensory ligaments which are attached in turn to the ciliary muscles. Contraction of the ciliary muscles reduces the tension on the lens which becomes more spherical. The ciliary muscle is innervated by parasympathetic nerve fibers in the third cranial nerve.

Pupillary Responses to Light

The activity of the iris regulates the size of the pupil and the amount of light entering the eye. The activity of the iris is regulated by two groups of smooth muscles. The circular muscles are more or less concentric fibers around the pupil. Contraction of these muscles which are controlled by the sympathetic nervous system decreases the size of the pupil. Relaxation of the circular fibers dilates the pupil. The radial muscles run as spokes in a wheel. Contraction of these fibers, which are controlled by the parasympathetic nervous system, increases the size of the pupil. Relaxation of the radial fibers constricts the pupil.

In addition to reflex accommodation, near and far vision, and the pupillary reflex to light, there are a number of other reflexes which are contributory or protective in the visual process.

Fixation—A quick movement toward a light in an effort to produce a focus on the fovea.

Fusion—Orientation of the two eyes so that the image is focused on on corresponding points of the two retinas. This results in fusion of the two images.

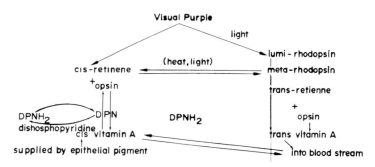

FIG. 2—*Schematic representation of the chemical reaction in the conversion of light to nerve impulses.*

Static—Reflexes originating in the inner ear and in the muscles of the neck tend to maintain the position of the head and thus to retain the visual field in its normal orientation.

Statokinetic—Rotation of the head produces a movement of the eyes in a direction opposite to the rotation. This tends to retain the visual field. When fixation can no longer be maintained, the eyes move quickly in the direction of rotation of the head in an effort to obtain a new field of focus. A continuation of the rotation results in a series of jerky oscillations of the eyes. The oscillating movements are known as nystagmus. Experimentally, this can be produced by: (*a*) rotation of the head; (*b*) placing warm or cold water in the ear which causes the predominant eye movement toward the warmer ear; (*c*) increase of pressure in the semicircular canals which produces the fast movement away from the side of pressure; (*d*) electrical stimulation which causes the fast motion towards the cathode; and (*e*) drug action on the labyrinths.

Acoustic reflex—Reflex movement of the eyes in the direction of a sudden sound.

Palpebral reflexes—The eye lids protect the eyes from irritating vapors or particles and also from glare or excessive light. In addition the lids tend to sweep foreign matter from the eyes. The blink reflex may be caused by any irritating or painful stimulus acting on the lids, conjunctiva, or the cornea. A blink reflex evoked by stimulation of the cornea is known as the corneal reflex. It has been used frequently as a test for depth of anesthesia. The optical blink reflex results from sudden flashes of light into the eye, or sudden movements near the eye.

Reflex lacrimation—The secretion of tears may be produced by reflex or any irritation of the cornea of conjunctiva, or also in association with sneezing, coughing, yawning, or vomiting.

The Retina

The retina is the light sensitive coat of the eye, and it is made up of several layers. One of these layers is composed of neurons known as rods and cones. These are the cells which are stimulated by light to produce the nerve impulse. The impulses pass over the other layers of the retina to the optic nerve, and then to the lateral geniculate bodies, and finally to the optic radiation and occipital cortex of the brain.

One of the steps in conversion of light to nerve impulses involves photochemical reactions. A pigment known as visual purple or rhodopsin is found in the rods. Possibly another pigment is contained in the cones. Light acts upon rhodopsin to produce new substances, and in the process the nerve impulse is generated. Rhodopsin must be quickly resynthesized, or the system would cease to function. The metabolites of rhodopsin must be removed, or the visual sensation would continue after cessation of the light stimulus. A schematic representation of the chemical reactions is shown in Fig. 2.

Flicker

When the retina is stimulated by a series of light flashes there is an alteration of light and darkness, and a sensation of flicker results. As the frequency of stimulation increases the flicker disappears and is replaced by the sensation of continuous light. The frequency at which this occurs is known as the critical fusion frequency (CFF).

After Images

Images sometimes remain in consciousness after the stimulus has ceased acting upon the eye. This is believed to result from a continuation of retinal changes brought about by the stimulus. Positive after-images retain their normal colors—negative after-images appear as complementary colors.

Dark Adaptation

On passing from light into darkness there is a brief period of blindness followed by progressively improved vision. The adaptation to the low intensity of light is associated with dilation of the pupil and increased sensitivity of the retina.

Light Adaptation

On passing from the dark into the light the eye is dazzled temporarily. Adaptation to the increased brightness is brought about by constriction of the pupil and decreased sensitivity of the retina.

Night and Day Blindness

In night blindness vision is defective in dim light while day and color vision is normal. Night blindness may be hereditary, but it is usually associated with Vitamin A deficiency which interferes with dark adaptation. Day blindness is characterized by defective color senses and photophobia.

Color Vision

Color vision is generally attributed to the cones and the light adapted eye. The hue depends upon the wavelength of the light. Brightness is the intensity of the light. Saturation is the purity of the wavelength or color involved.

The Young-von Helmholtz theory of color vision is the best known. The theory postulates three types of receptors each sensitive to one of the primary colors. Color sensations result from stimulation of three elements at different relative intensities. Color blindness is explained on the basis that red, green, or blue sensitive substances are defective or absent.

H. R. Silbiger[1]

Hearing

REFERENCE: Silbiger, H. R., **Hearing,** *Basic Principles of Sensory Evaluation, ASTM STP 433,* American Society for Testing and Materials, 1968, pp. 24–29.

Sound is the perception by humans of vibrations in some physical medium, usually air. These physical vibrations of the air are evidenced by alternating rarefractions and compressions. Man's primary sense organ for the sound stimulus is the ear (Fig. 1). The external ear consists of the pinna or auricle. From this a canal, the auditory meatus, leads into the skull. This canal terminates at the eardrum, or tympanic membrane. A small muscle, the tensor tympani, regulates the tension of the tympanic membrane.

Beyond the tympanic membrane is the middle ear. The sound transmission path in the middle ear from the tympanic membrane is by means of three small, interconnected bones, the ossicles (malleus, incus, stapes).

The stapes is connected to the oval window, which is part of the separation between the middle and inner ear. The inner ear, or cochlea, is a spirally coiled fluid-filled canal in the temporal bone. It is divided along its length by the basilar membrane and the vestibular membrane. On the basilar membrane are found the hair cells. The vibrations which entered the cochlea through the tympanic membrane, ossicles, and oval window give rise to hydraulic motion in the cochlea. This causes the basilar membrane to move as a traveling wave. The basilar membrane motion stimulates the hair cells and causes them to emit nerve impulses. These nerve impulses then travel along the auditory (VIII) nerve to the brain. Acoustic vibrations have two major physical dimensions, amplitude and frequency. These give rise to the psychological dimensions of loudness and pitch. The three major operations of the hearing mechanism upon the sound stimulus are: detection, discrimination, and identification.

Sound amplitude is normally expresed as a function of the sound pressure level at a specified point. The sound pressure level (SPL) is measured in decibels above a reference level. The United States of America

[1] Bell Telephone Laboratories, Inc., Holmdel, N. J.

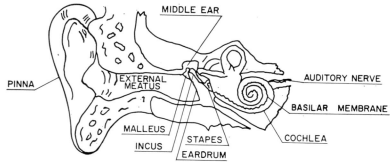

FIG. 1—*Cross section of the human ear.*

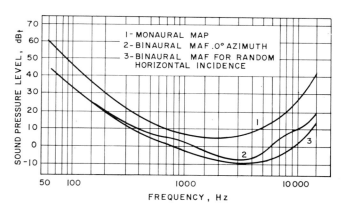

FIG. 2—*Auditory thresholds for young adults. MAP = minimum audible pressure, earphones. MA = minimum audible field. (From Sivian, L. J. and White, S. D., "On Minimum Audible Sound Fields," Journal of the Acoustical Society of America, Vol. 4, 1933, pp. 288–321.)*

Standard reference level for sound pressure is 0.00002 newtons/m².[2] Decibels referred to this level maybe symbolized as dBt.

Sound frequency is measured in Hertz,[3] symbolized as Hz.

Detection

In order for a sound stimulus to be detected, it must attain a certain minimum sound pressure level at the eardrum. The weakest signal which gives rise to a sensation which is just barely detectable as sound[4] is called the auditory threshold. The amplitude of the signal at threshold varies as a function of the frequency of the signal (Fig. 2). In adults, the detectable frequency range is from 30 to 15,000 Hz. The ear is not equally

[2] Equivalent to 0.0002 dynes/cm² or 2 microbars.
[3] Previously cycles per second, cps, c/s.
[4] Usually statistically defined as a correct detection 50 per cent better than the change level.

sensitive at all frequencies but is most sensitive in the range from 500 to 4000 Hz. A set of values has been adopted by the International Standards Organization (ISO) as the reference normal hearing threshold (Table 1). These numbers are based on the thresholds of an international sample of normal young adults. The detection ability of an individual can then be expressed with these values as reference levels. The difference, in decibels, between the ISO threshold level, and the threshold SPL for the individual at a particular frequency is called the hearing level (HL) in dB re ISO 1964.[5] Hearing impairment at a particular frequency from a medico-legal standpoint in some states is considered to exist when the HL exceeds +25 dB. The line connecting the individual's HL points over the frequencies where it was determined is called an audiogram, and shows how his threshold deviates from the norm. As individuals age, their threshold of audibility gradually increases for frequencies above 3000 Hz. This phenomenon is called

TABLE 1—*Earphone sound pressure levels at threshold according to ISO R389-1964.*

Frequency, Hz	Sound Pressure level, dBt
125	45.5
250	24.5
500	11.0
1000	6.5
2000	8.5
3000	7.5
4000	9.0
6000	8.0
8000	9.5

presbyacusis. Factors such as aural disease and exposure to excessive stimulation may also cause elevation of the threshold (deafness).

Another quantity used in hearing is the sensation level (SL). This is the difference between the sound pressure level of a stimulus and the individual's threshold SPL for this stimulus.

The range of audibility also has an upper bound. At levels higher than 120 dBt the sensation of sound is replaced by one of feeling.

Discrimination

A signal has to differ from another by a definite amount to be distinguished as different. This minimal increment is called the just noticeable difference, the difference threshold or difference limen (DL). The DL is defined statistically by the fraction of correct discriminations.

[5] Normal hearing levels according to USASI Z21.4-1951 are somewhat higher, and are in the process of revision to conform to ISO R389-1964.

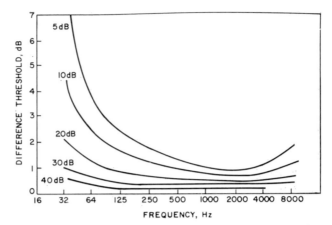

FIG. 3—*Difference thresholds for intensity. Sensation levels as indicated. (From Riesz, R. R., "Differential Sensitivity of the Ear for Pure Tones,"* Physical Review, *Vol. 3, pp. 867–875, 1928.)*

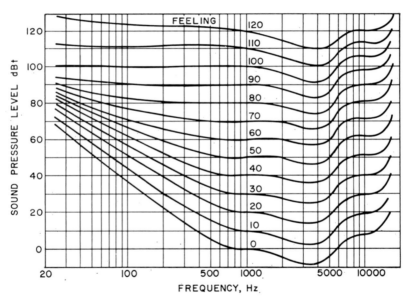

FIG. 4—*Equal loudness contours. (From Fletcher, H. and Munson, W. A., "Loudness, Its Definition, Measurement, and Calculation,"* Journal of the Acoustical Society of America, *Vol. 5, 1933, pp. 82–108.)*

Difference limens may be determined, among others, for amplitude and frequency.

Amplitude Discrimination

An increase in the intensity level of an auditory stimulus gives rise to an increase in the loudness of that stimulus. The minimum difference in level between two tones of the same frequency that can be discriminated is called the intensity difference threshold, or intensity difference limen (IDL). The size of this intensity DL is a function of both the frequency and the SL of the tone (Fig. 3). Discrimination is finest at high levels and in the middle frequency range.

Two tones of equal SPL but differing in frequency may not have equal loudness. By setting the loudness of a test tone equal to the loudness of a 1000 Hz reference tone at a certain SPL, equal loudness contours may be plotted (Fig. 4). The zero loudness contour line is the auditory thresh-

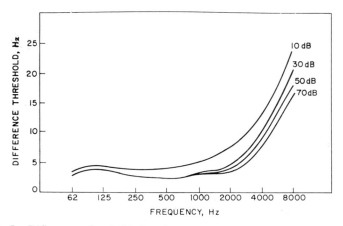

FIG. 5—*Difference threshold for frequency, sensation level 10 dB.* (*From Shower, E. G. and Biddulph, R., "Differential Pitch Sensitivity of the Ear,"* Journal of the Acoustical Society of America, *Vol. 3, 1931, pp. 275–287.*)

old. Sound pressure levels on each contour line give rise to sensations of equal loudness. For pure tones equal SPL's give rise to equal loudness at high levels, while at low levels a higher intensity is required at the extreme frequencies than at the middle frequencies to obtain a given loudness. The loudness relationships for noise are more complex. Methods for the calculation of the loudness of noise may be found in United States of America Standard USASI S3.4.

Frequency Discrimination

The audible frequency range extends from approximately 40 to 1500 Hz. Each frequency gives rise to a sensation of a certain pitch. Pitch is not only a function of the frequency of the stimulus tone, but also of its sound pressure level. For tones above 2000 Hz the pitch increases with intensity, while for those below 2000 Hz it decreases in intensity. This phenomenon is mainly noticeable on pure tones (sinusoids). The discrimination of differences in pitch between two tones is mainly a function of the frequency of the two tones, with some contribution made by level (Fig. 5). The DL for pitch is smallest at the low frequencies.

Identification

At very low levels, that is, at or below 5 dB SL there is little tonal sensation to a tone. At higher levels all tones have a definite pitch. The musical pitch of a tone may be given in musical notation (CDEFGAB). With training most individuals can match a given tone, or name the pitch of a tone when given a reference tone. Most individuals do not have the ability to name the pitch of a tone on an absolute basis without the use of a reference tone.

Masking

A tone may be rendered inaudible by the simultaneous addition of another tone or a noise at higher SPL. This phenomenon is called masking. This masking effect for tones by tones is greater when the two tones are close in frequency but extends throughout the entire auditory range. Masking is also greater in the high frequency direction, that is, a tone will mask another of higher frequency easier than one of lower frequency. In the case of masking by a band of noise, tones may be masked by noise only within a critical band centered about the tone. The width of the critical band increases with the center frequency of the critical band. Noise outside this critical band does not mask the tone to a great extent.

Temporary Threshold Shift

Extended exposure to levels of stimulation above 85 dBt produces a gradual loss of auditory sensitivity called temporary threshold shift (TTS). The greatest amount of shift takes place one-half octave above the frequency of the stimulus tone. The amount of shift is a function of the level and the duration of the stimulus tone. Recovery from TTS is logarithmic with time. However, if the TTS 2 min after exposure (TTS_2) is more than 40 dB, recovery is linear with time, and the original threshold may not be reached. A permanent hearing loss may have occurred. Criteria for exposure to loud stimulation have been established.

Summary

Auditory perception is a function of acoustic stimulation by vibrations of a frequency range between 30 Hz and 15000 Hz and intensity levels between 0 dBt and 120 dBt. Frequency and intensity discrimination varies widely as a function of the frequency and intensity of the stimulus tones.

Herbert Stone[1] and R. M. Pangborn[2]

Intercorrelation of the Senses

REFERENCE: Stone, Herbert and Pangborn, R. M., **"Intercorrelation of the Senses,"** *Basic Principles of Sensory Evaluation, ASTM STP 433,* American Society for Testing and Materials, 1968, pp. 30–46.

Receptors, such as the eye, the ear, the organs of smell and taste, and the more diffuse sensory equipment of the skin, are found in all higher animals. Not all of the senses are equally helpful to the organism; the hawk's keen visual acuity is well documented, as is the bat's auditory sensitivity to meaningful echoes and the bloodhound's perception of olfactory clues. Although man derives comfort from touch and the pleasures of odors and tastes, his world is largely regulated by sound and light, calling into play the senses he finds most valuable in communication, navigation, and detection of objects at a distance. The conception of size, shape and color, or proximity and remoteness of light and shade, assist us in relating to our environment to a much greater degree than do the other senses. For example, texture, essentially a function of touch, can be conveyed visually from distant objects, after the individual has had sufficient preliminary experience. Through experience and association, we can conceptualize sensations of sound, touch, pain, temperature, taste, and odor by merely viewing the stimulus object. Misjudgments, of course, are known to occur.

We respond to environmental stimuli through all avenues of sensory input, and, although the extent of their interrelationship is not well understood, it is generally accepted that the stimulation of one sense organ influences to some degree the sensitivity of the organs of another sense. Whether the influence is exerted upon the receptors or upon their central areas in the cortex is not known with certainty. Sherrington's [1][3] statement bears quoting: "All parts of the nervous system are connected together and no part of it is probably ever capable of reaction without af-

---

[1] Head, Olfaction Research Laboratory, Division of Life Sciences, Stanford Research Institute, Menlo Park, Calif.

[2] Assistant professor, Food Science and Technology, University of California, Davis, Calif.

[3] The italic numbers in brackets refer to the list of references appended to this paper.

fecting and being affected by various other parts, and it is a system certainly never absolutely at rest."

The Chemical Senses

The olfactory organs, the vomero-nasal organs, the common chemical receptors, and the organs of taste form a natural group of organs generally called chemical receptors or chemo-receptors. The stimulus for the chemo-receptor is a solution of chemically active material which must come in direct contact with the terminal organ. This requirement distinguishes chemo-receptors from mechanico-receptors, which can be stimulated from a distance. In many animals, particularly aquatic species, the distinctions among gustation, the common chemical sense, and olfaction may seem somewhat arbitrary. Once taken into the mouth, foods and beverages make at least a dual, usually a triple, appeal. The tissues of the mouth, throat, and nasal cavity are so innervated, and so disposed in relation to one another, that any or all of three sensory systems operate simultaneously in response to the same stimulus. The cutaneous sensibilities of the mouth region react to texture and astringency, as well as biting, burning, cooling, and tingle. The sense of taste is also obviously involved, but it is olfaction that furnishes the most elaborate experiences connected with food flavor. Behaviorally, then, it is difficult to partition the chemical senses and even to separate them from other oral sensations when the stimuli are placed in the mouth.

There is no question of the distinctness of the human sensations attributed to the common chemical (or trigeminal) sense contrasted with our sensations of smell, taste, touch, or pain. The fact that taste always involves specialized end organs, such as taste buds, whereas receptive surfaces for chemical irritants may contain only free-nerve endings, shows that the relation of these two classes of receptors is at best only distant. The curious feeling that comes from vapors that irritate the eyes, nose, or even the mouth has not the remotest relation to touch, smell or taste, and is only distantly suggestive of pain. Pain, however, is easily separated from the common chemical sense by the use of cocaine; therefore, it is concluded that the common chemical sense is a true sense with an independent set of receptors (free nerve endings) and a sensation quality entirely its own.

Gustation, olfaction, and the common chemical sense are as separate and distinct as vision and audition as shown by the following evidence: (1) Psychological: the qualities are quite different. Compare the experiences of the taste of salt, the odor of leather, and the bite of chili; (2) Physiological: by taking advantage of disease or injury, or by the use of nacrotics such as cocaine, it has been possible to show that any one of the three senses may be eliminated, leaving the other undisturbed; (3)

Anatomical: the neural pathways in the central nervous system are separate and distinct, as shown below:

Cranial Nerve	Name	Structure Innervated
1st..........	olfactory	olfactory mucosa
5th..........	trigeminal	free nerve endings (common chemical sense) masticatory muscles
7th..........	facial	face muscles, salivary glands; taste buds of anterior two thirds of tongue
9th..........	glossopharyngeal	swallowing reflex; taste buds of posterior one third of tongue
12th..........	hypoglossal	tongue muscles

Many sensations commonly attributed to taste are in fact, "flavor," which is a combination of taste and odor (see section on Flavor). Since airborne volatile substances are detected by smell, it has been loosely described as "taste at a distance." Some organisms have been observed to reject—possibly through the common chemical sense—chlorine, sulfuric acid, or picric acid in strong concentrations, whereas these substances are sometimes attractive in very low concentrations.

Gustatory-olfactory

The grouping of the olfactory and gustatory receptors at the entrance to the respiratory and alimentary tracts of air-inhabiting animals strongly suggests that these senses are frequently stimulated in combination. Tastes, by definition, are limited to oral sensations of sweet (exemplified by sucrose), sour (citric acid), salty (sodium chloride), and bitter (quinine). The qualities of odors, in contrast, appear to be almost innumerable. The highly trained nose can distinguish over a thousand different odors, but no classification of odor stimuli into primary categories has proved to be completely satisfactory. Early attempts at classification confounded quality, intensity, taste factors, and hedonic tone (like and dislike). The lack of general correlation between chemical constitution of odorous or sapid substances with the sensation they provoke may merely reflect the lack of our understanding of the surface phenomena of receptor cells. Unlike the names for taste qualities, the names for odors are derived by association—it smells *like* roses, onions, rubber, etc. Also unlike taste, smell figures prominently in association and memory; a slight odor may recall long chains of events and experiences which may have occurred years before or even in childhood. Mixtures of sapid solutions do not as a rule give rise to tastes other than those of their components. Lemonade has both the sweet taste of the sugar and the sour taste of the citric acid. Odor mixtures, however, can generate entirely new olfactory sensations in which individual components cannot be recognized. Olfactory adaptation appears to occur much more rapidly and is more prolonged than is gustatory adaptation.

Many compounds stimulate both taste and odor responses, since inhaled vapors can descend readily from the nose to the oropharyngeal area, and, conversely, oral stimuli can emit volatiles to stimulate the upper olfactory region. The effective quantity of volatile compounds, however, is generally much lower for smell than for taste. Ethyl alcohol, for example, could be smelled at $1/8000\ M$ and in some instances as low as $1/400,000\ M$, whereas the taste threshold was $3\ M$ (Parker and Stabler, [2]). The most active of sapid substances, strychnine, gives a bitter sensation at a molecular concentration of 1 ppm, but the odor of mercaptan can be perceived in 0.02-ppm air. Differential sensitivity to taste, however, appears to be finer than that to odor. Fatigue is also more rapid and longer lasting with smell than with taste, sight, or hearing.

In studies on the interaction between olfactory and taste sensations, von Békésy [3] observed that by varying the time delay between stimuli (one to the nose, the other to the tongue), it was possible to make the combined sensation move from the tip of the nose to the throat and then again forward to the tip of the tongue. In the nose, the combined sensation showed all the characteristics of a purely olfactory stimulus and on the tongue, that of pure taste. It was only on the back of the tongue and throat that a combination of the two sensations occurred.

Using methyl, ethyl, and propyl alcohol at near-threshold concentrations as stimulants of olfactory, taste, and trigeminal receptors, Mitchell [4] observed that smell was the most sensitive and irritance the least sensitive sense. Olfactory thresholds were lower when measured as a single task than as a combined task, but it is unclear whether the differences were due to intermodal effects, to artifacts of the different methods of measurement, or both. Mitchell suggests that the hedonic aspects (degree of liking) of the stimuli may contribute to interactive sensory response.

When considering differences and similarities between the senses of taste and smell, the role of saliva in affecting the former (but not necessarily the latter) must be borne in mind. The amount of saliva secreted, the rate of secretion, its viscosity, and its chemical composition could, conceivably, influence interpretation of taste and tactile stimuli.

Although the receptors for taste are located in the oral cavity in close proximity with olfactory, cutaneous, kinesthetic, and thermal receptors, there is functional as well as anatomical evidence of separate cortical localization of these systems (Börnstein, [5]). Anatomically, the gustatory system bears very little similarity to the olfactory system but has essential points in common with the somato-sensory system.

In critical experimentation, it may be necessary to separate responses due to gustatory cues from those due to olfactory stimulation. Benjamin

[6] reported that in rats, removal of the olfactory bulbs had no effect on taste preference for quinine hydrochloride. Using conditioned avoidance techniques with electric shock, however, significantly increased "taste" thresholds. These results suggest that the quinine solutions provided the animal with olfactory cues.

Gustatory-tactile

One of the earliest studies on the interrelationship of the tactile and gustatory properties of oral stimuli was reported by von Skramlik [7]. He stated that intensity of taste is greater in aqueous media than in paraffin oil, a condition which may be related to the combined effects of viscosity, solubility of the compounds in oil, and of the oil in saliva. It might be speculated that the physical state of an oral stimulus could influence taste by partially controlling the quantity of sapid matter reaching the receptors in a given time.

In experiments conducted by Mackey and Valassi [8], taste thresholds for sucrose, sodium chloride, caffeine, and tartaric acid were lower in water solutions than in tomato juice and custard, each prepared as liquids, gels, and foams. The added taste substances were easiest to detect in the liquid state, most difficult in the gel, and intermediate in the foam. Later, Mackey [9] observed that the tastes of caffeine, quinine, and saccharine were more easily detected in water than in mineral oil and theorized that the lipid inhibited the solubility of the taste compounds in the saliva. When methylcellulose was added to water to produce the viscosity of oil, ease of detection of the three compounds was intermediate between water and oil.

More recent experiments by Stone and Oliver [10] corroborated the earlier studies that taste detection thresholds were decreased with increasing viscosity; however, at suprathreshold concentrations, the sweetness of sucrose solutions increased with increasing viscosity.

Börnstein [5] indicated that the gustatory system has a close anatomical relation to the somato-sensory system. He presented five lines of evidence for believing that the cortical taste center is localized in the neighborhood of the cortical tactile representation of the parts carrying taste buds, that is, tongue, soft palate, pharynx, and epiglottis:

1. *Functional relations between taste and tactile sensibility*—Under biological conditions, all gustatory stimuli act at the same time upon organs for touch (or pressure) and temperature. Tactile and gustatory perceptions may merge to build an intersensory complex impossible to analyze into its components. For example, salts in appropriate concentrations act simultaneously on taste, touch, and pain nerve endings. Lye produces seemingly, a simple "alkaline taste," but in fact this sensation is built up of gustatory, olfactory, pain, temperature, and touch perceptions.

The astringent action of acids is not perceived by the gustatory sense but by tactile sensibility.

2. *Structure of the receptor*—The olfactory end organ retains a primitive type of structure consisting of a single cell in the periphery performing both a receptive and a conductive function. The gustatory and tactile sensory systems, however, consist of a chain of two links, that is, special sensory cells which receive the stimulus and of nerve fibers (teledendrons) arborizing around them, which run to their centrally situated cell bodies, ganglion cells.

3. *First-order neurons*—Olfactory axons are initially unmyelinated, develop from bipolar cells in the olfactory epithelium in the periphery, and connect with the olfactory bulb and then via the olfactory lobe to a part of the telencephalon. The gustatory fibers run in mixed sensory and motor nerves; they develop from ganglia and are myelinated, connecting with the myelencephalon. Gustatory fibers run in cerebral nerves which either conduct tactile sensory impulses in man, or did so in earlier phylogenetic stages. There is some evidence that gustation may be a derived tactile sense.

4. *Second-order neurons*—There is clinical evidence to suggest that the gustatory pathway not only runs in the neighborhood of tactile fibers within the medulla oblongata and pons, but   probably also terminates adjacent to them in the thalamus.

5. *Sensory-motor relations*—Motor and sensory areas for the face are in close topographical as well as functional relations. Gustatory sensation, like the somatic sensations from mouth parts, is related to chewing and tongue movements.

Gustatory-visual

The interaction of taste and appearance is especially operative in foods. We associate discoloration, color fading, shriveling of the surface, and other alterations in visual properties with altered flavor and tactile qualities. A few studies have been reported on the influence of color on taste and flavor. Moir [11] noted that subjects almost invariably identified fruit flavors incorrectly when jellies were atypically colored. Kanig [12] found that few of 200 pharmacy students tested could identify flavorings presented in colorless syrups, and even fewer responded correctly when solutions were presented in unusual colors. The influence of previous experience upon color and flavor was operative in a study by Dunker [13] in which white chocolate was considered to taste less like chocolate than the customary brown product. Hall [14] described an experiment in which sherbets in six flavors were prepared in their natural or commonly associated color, in an inappropriate color, and uncolored. As anticipated, subjects were highly successful in identifying flavors presented in their customary colors, less so with flavors presented in uncolored form, and very unsuccessful with sherbets colored deceptively.

According to Pangborn [15] sweetness discrimination was not influenced by red, green, or yellow coloring in unflavored aqueous solutions. In pear nectar, in contrast, there was a pronounced tendency to designate the green-colored samples as the least sweet. Also, pink-colored table wines were thought to be sweeter than white, light red, dark red, or light brown-colored wines of the same composition, by experienced subjects but not by a naive panel.

Allen and Schwartz [16] applied quinine sulfate to the tongue and measured the critical fusion frequency. This measure (cff) is the frequency, in cycles per second, at which a flickering light is perceived as a steady light. Red sensation was depressed and green enhanced in sensitivity over the normal levels following quinine administration. When a rest period of 3 min was allowed between the cessation of taste stimulation and measurement of visual responses, there was a reversal, so that red sensations were enhanced and green depressed in sensitivity. Under both conditions the violet sensations were depressed. It is of interest that sucrose produced no visual effect.

London [17] cited Russian experiments in which weak sugar, salt, and acid solutions increased peripheral visual sensitivity, whereas quinine induced a decrease. The effect of the latter compound was attributed to the negative reaction of the subject to the bitterness of quinine. Electrical sensitivity of vision and taste under the influence of optical and taste stimuli has been studied by Dobriakova [18]. When sugar furnished the accessory stimulus, electrical sensitivity was increased; where the stimulus was salt or citric acid, it was reduced. Stimulation by bright illumination after dark adaptation increased electrical sensitivity of both the tongue and the eye. Electrical sensitivity of the gustatory apparatus, as well as sensitivity to salt solution, is reported to have decreased in the course of dark adaptation of the eye. Tronova [19] measured change of sensitivity to sodium chloride under three conditions of light: no light, a "normal" condition, and 350 lux. In general, sensitivity increased with the amount of light, but individual differences were large, and the reliability of results could be questioned.

Following visual deprivation, Schutte and Zubek [20] observed a significant increase in taste sensitivity to salt and sucrose with the effect lasting for one day after restoration of normal visual stimuli. Sensitivity to sour and bitter stimuli, however, were unchanged.

A detailed study on the influence of ambient lighting on perceived intensity of the acid taste was reported by Gregson [21]. Subjective intensities of three concentrations of citric acid were evaluated by 24 subjects under four levels of illumination. Two major conclusions were: (1) there was a small intersensory effect of ambient light on perceived relative intensity of acid tastes, facilitatory for most subjects but negative for others, and (2) the intersensory effect was multiplicative, that is, it is not readily explained as a simple threshold shift effect. Gregson raises a valid point of criticism of previous work in which mean responses rather than individual subject responses are frequently used in analyses of data, thereby losing information on individual differences in intersensory facilitation or inhibition.

Becker and Morton [22] raise the question concerning the nature of the association between phenylthiourea taste sensitivity (genetically determined) and glaucoma. A high percentage (53 per cent) of nontasters were found in patients with primary open-angle glaucoma, which differed significantly from the 27 per cent nontasters among nonglaucomic individuals.

Vitamin A has been implicated in taste (Bernard et al [23]) and olfaction (Duncan and Briggs [24]) as well as in vision. Since supplementation of deficient subjects with the vitamin improved taste and olfactory responses, it is speculated that the vitamin may have an effect on the integrity of the epithelial tissue of these structures and not be directly involved in stimulatory process (Moulton [25]).

Gustatory-Auditory

Only a few isolated reports are available on the interrelationships of the chemical senses with sound. In a preliminary test, Srinivasan [26] found that the response to the sweetness of sucrose and the saltiness of sodium chloride differed with the ears closed and the ears open. When hearing was blocked by placing the palms against the ears, many subjects ascribed tastes other than sweetness to the sugars, whereas others found either enhancement or depression of sweetness intensity. With salt, most subjects recorded changes in intensity when the ears were closed.

The effect of quiet and controlled sound (tape recording of clattering dishes and muffled voices at 80 dB) on flavor preferences for tomato juice was tested by Pettit [27]. Neither the test location nor the background noise altered preferences significantly. The effect of noise or sound on other sensory modalities varies greatly among individuals, as some are more easily distracted than others. If noises irritate the subject, the internal distraction is worse than mere noise.

Olfactory-Tactile

The literature makes little or no reference to investigations on the interaction of olfaction with tactile stimuli, perhaps because the two do not appear to be logically associated functionally or anatomically. It would seem reasonable, however, that any alteration in the physical form of an oral stimulus could alter the behavior of its volatile components by changing vapor pressure or rate of release of constituents. Dispersion of an odorous compound in a tasteless, odorless gum could conceivably depress apparent odor intensity. To test this independent of the perception of oral viscosity would necessitate controlled experimental testing by sniffing ("aroma") versus odor by mouth ("flavor").

Olfactory-visual

The appearance of an object certainly influences our anticipation of its odor properties, but there is little information on the interaction of these two modalities. Hoeven-Leonard [28] postulated a connection between low color sensitivity and high olfactory acuity, but seems to have made no definite studies. Earlier, Fauvelle [29] had suggested that forms of life with a prominent naso-labial organ frequently have limited vision. He believed that this applied to individuals and to races of people.

Olfactory stimuli were found by Russian investigators to influence extra-foveal visual sensitivity, generally enhancing it, but also decreasing sensitivity if unpleasant (London [17]). It is of interest that the reciprocity between vision and olfaction was also found between vision and audition and between vision and gustation, that is, white light was claimed to increase olfactory and gustatory sensitivity.

According to Russian investigations, the odor of bergamot oil and of pyridine in toluol, for example, heightened peripheral sensitivity of the visual organ, although where there were strong negative reactions to the latter, instances of lowered sensitivity were reported (London [17]). Under the olfactory action of bergamot oil, an increase in threshold of electrical sensitivity was reported.

With brightness of flicker acting upon the central retina so as to produce a critical flicker frequency (cff) of 12 to 18 flashes per second for an eye at a specified level of dark adaptation, the odors of bergamot oil and geraniol reduced cff for green-blue illumination and increased it for orange-red (London [17]). No effects were noted for yellow (570 millimicrons) or for extreme spectral red (690 millimicrons) and violet (425 millimicrons). Furthermore, on cessation of accessory action, it was found that cff returned not only to previous levels, but having done so, often proceeded to exhibit relative frequencies the reverse of those obtained previously under olfactory influences. The odor of bergamot oil was also found to increase the threshold of electrical sensitivity of the eye. Color zone boundaries were reported to shift under the influence of accessory stimulation. The odor of rosemary resulted in expansion of the green region and indol resulted in contraction. Rosemary was found to contract the red zone and indol, to expand it.

Oil of geranium, oil of cassia, and vanillin were used as stimulating substances by Allen and Schwartz [16], who then measured cff. With the first substance, the red and violet sensations were depressed in sensitivity and the green enhanced. With the other two substances similar results were obtained, except that they were not extended into the blue-violet region of the spectrum. Allowing a 45-min rest between stimulation with oil of cassia, the cff measurement showed a reversal of sensitivity of all three color sensations—red and violet were enhanced and green depressed in sensitivity. It should be borne in mind that odorous compounds which irritate the free nerve endings could stimulate the eye as well as the nasal area. Many olfactory stimuli are capable of stimulating these trigeminal receptors at low concentrations (Beidler [30], Dawson [31], Moulton [32], Stone et al [33].

Olfactory-Auditory

There appears to be little relationship between the olfactory and auditory modalities except as one may be associated with the other through conditioning. It is possible that presentation of one stimulus in the presence of another may distract the subject sufficiently to decrease or delay the response. Hernández-Peón et al [34] reported that auditory-evoked potentials were reduced when cats were attentive to visual, olfactory, or somatic stimuli. An olfactory analog to directional hearing was postulated by von Békésy [3], who measured the time difference and the difference in sensation magnitude of olfactory stimuli between the two nostrils as the air surrounding the odorous material was inhaled. The direction of an odor could be determined with a precision of 7 to 10 deg in spite of the small distance between the nostrils compared with the distance between the ears.

According to Russian studies, auditory thresholds were lowered when the odors of geraniol and benzol supplied the accessory stimulation (London [17]).

Optical, Tactile, and Acoustical Modalities

Comparatively little work has been done where the primary stimulus has not been visual or auditory. What has been published, mainly by Russian laboratories, shows the presence of accessory effects. London [17] has summarized and discussed the field, citing 506 references. Owing to language difficulties and the near unavailability of the literature, most of the experimental and theoretical work done in the Soviet Union has gone unnoticed. London warns that the Soviet literature contains ready evidence of use of inadequate instrumentation and methodology, scanty detail, and a primitiveness in the statistical treatment of data. Another negative factor is the discouragement encountered by the difficulty in attempting to duplicate the reported findings. Nonetheless, unlike western work, the subject of sensory interaction has received systematic and sustained attention in the Soviet Union.

Visual-Auditory

The senses which seem to be best adapted for the purpose of measure-ment of sense modality interaction are those of hearing and vision. As long ago as 1888, Urbantschitsch [35] observed that sounds of different tones may act differently upon the sensitivity of the visual apparatus for various colors, but detected no definite quantitative relation between sound and color. Later, Lazarev [36] observed that the visual sen-sibility of the retinal periphery (rod vision) increased under the influence of acoustical stimulation of the ear. Yakovlev [37] found that stimula-tion of the ear by sound conspicuously enlarged the area of the field of cone vision especially for green light. Kravkov [38] reported that under the influence of sound the critical frequency of flicker of white light increased for central or cone vision, and diminished for peripheral or rod vision.

Yakovlev [39] studied the influence of acoustic stimulation, both by musical tones of frequency 780 Hz and noises of 75 dB in loudness, upon the limits of the areas of the retinal fields for extreme red, orange-red, green, and blue colors. Under the influence of both tones and noises the color field for extreme red was unaltered, that for orange-red diminished, and those for green and blue, enlarged in area. Noise was more effective as a stimulus than musical tone, possibly because of its greater intensity, and under its influence the color fields were diminished and enlarged to the greatest extent.

Results of the Russian investigations indicating that sensitivity to white light in the fovea is increased under auditory stimulation of moderate intensity are not surprising, as the effect may simply reflect a generalized state of heightened sensitivity in the subject, that is, the auditory stimulation may help keep the subject alert in an otherwise monotonous environment. It is surprising, however, that the effect of the auditory stimulation depends on the wave length of the light stimulus. It was found that auditory stimulation increased sensitivity to blue-green light, but that it lowered sensitivity to orange-red light. Other hues were unaffected. This would suggest a more direct link between the auditory and visual systems than a simple mutual dependence upon the general alertness of the subject.

Thompson et al [40] studied the effects of different intensities of simul-taneous illumination on the detection threshold for a 1000 cycle tone. It was found that the auditory detection threshold decreased under these conditions. This evidence supports some of the Russian research, al-though Dember [41] feels that the test technique used (the method of limits) is susceptible to error.

It has been shown by Livanov [42] that if animals are exposed to trains of synchronous flashes and clicks, after a given time the same flash rate, without clicks, will produce a repetitive response in the auditory cortex.

This result can be confirmed in cortical recordings, but it is not known whether this intermixing of the sense modalities could be detected in the deeper structures of the brain.

Monaural stimulation with two tones (150 and 1200 Hz) at two intensities produced altered visual responses to critical frequency of flicker (Allen and Schwartz [16]). With no rest interval between stimulation and measurement, the red and violet colors of this spectrum appeared of lowered and the green of enhanced intensity. Allowing a 3-min rest between the auditory stimulation and the visual measurement resulted in a complete reversal of sensitivity of the red and green sensations.

Walker and Sawyer [43] reported that the cff for monocular vision had a tendency to increase when random noise pulsed in-phase with an intermittent visual stimulus was included in the test. After addition of an artificial pupil, the noise had no effect on the cff. Small [44] sugggested that the sensory interaction might operate through the system which controls pupil size.

The effects of auditory stimulation on cff depended on the monochromatic nature of the light used (London [17]). During auditory action pitched at 800 cycles at 85 dB, cff for green light at 520 millimicrons was reduced, whereas for orange-red light at 630 millimicrons, cff was raised. With white light as the primary stimulus, accessory auditory action was also found to affect cff; for central vision it was heightened, for peripheral vision, lowered.

London [17] discussed studies in the Russian literature in which peripheral visual sensitivity declined on exposure to sounds of average or above average intensity. For example, the noise of an airplane motor actually dropped peripheral sensitivity to as low as 20 per cent of the level under quiet conditions. A brief period of hyperventilation, however, was held to restore peripheral sensitivity despite continued auditory stimulation. Exposure to ultrasonic frequencies (for example, 32,800 Hz) was reported to increase peripheral sensitivity.

Relative to brightness, Russian workers reported that the brighter the viewed field, the greater the decrease in differential sensitivity under the effect of simultaneous auditory stimulation (London [17]). Very loud noises, such as those produced by an airplane motor, impaired general brightness discrimination markedly. It is possible that vibrations caused by such loud noises could cause the visual field to "bounce."

While most research has employed light as the primary stimulus, a number of Russian investigators have used sound as the primary tool (London [17]). Illumination of the eyes with white light, for example, was claimed to increase auditory sensitivity; absence of visual stimulation, on the contrary, decreased it. However, opposite effects were obtained by using different monochromatic lights; illumination of a white room with green light increased auditory sensitivity, but with red light, it was decreased.

Visual-Tactile

Conflicts between vision and touch concerning properties such as shape or size have been studied only recently. Rock and Victor [45] presented observers with objects through an optical element which caused distortion. When visual shapes differed considerably from tactile shapes, the visual impression was completely dominant. Visual clues also dominated tactile impressions in evaluating size. In general, the observer was unaware of the conflict between the two modalities. According to experiments with preschool children by Zinchenoko and Ruzskaia [46], the eyes teach the hand how to touch.

Axelrod [48] studied the effects of early blindness on perceptual performance in modalities other than vision with blind and sighted children. It was concluded that differences between groups were not consistent in any direction between early blind and sighted subjects for two-point limens and light-touch sensitivity. Stellwagen and Culbert [47] found no differences in the ability of 50 blind and 50 sighted subjects to discriminate tactually among ten embossed textural patterns.

Tactile-Auditory

The sounds emitted by an object tell us little about its tactile properties, except through association, as when the fizz of a carbonated beverage causes us to anticipate prickling sensations on the lips and tongue. We frequently encounter auditory-kinesthetic associations in foods, for example, the sounds and textures of crisp lettuce, fresh celery, and hard candy. These associations are probably more significant than presently thought; however, appropriate experiments have not yet been undertaken.

As part of a study on vibrational properties of foodstuffs, Drake [49] analyzed the amplitude, frequency, and duration of the sounds produced in chewing. He speculated that mastication sounds and related vibrations are utilized by the subject as a complement to static clues in subjective estimation of the mechanical properties of food.

Flavor

Although referred to briefly in early sections of this discussion, flavor is sufficiently important to warrant further mention. Food scientists have devoted much effort to the evaluation of both the sensory and chemical counterparts of flavor. Since flavors are derived from the simultaneous stimulation of several senses: taste, smell, pressure, and cutaneous sense, and possibly, vision and audition, the interaction of these senses is of significance to the food scientist. Although there is an ever-increasing amount of literature on sensory flavor problems and volatile flavor chemistry, no attempt will be made to review this literature here. It is important to recognize that any sensory technique for flavor measurement should take these factors into account, since a deficiency in any one parameter will downgrade the overall flavor quality.

Conditions Influencing Sensory Interaction

Some conditions affecting sensory interaction, as well as theories on the mechanism of interaction, have been presented by London [17], who calls attention to the following factors:

1. *Strength of accessory stimulus*—Increase in strength of the accessory stimulus leads so often to effects that are the reverse of those induced by weaker intensities that one can almost speak of a "rule of inversion." For example, sounds of weak intensity heighten the electrical sensitivity of the eye, while those of increasing intensity are accompanied by a gradual decline. There are exceptions to this "rule," however.

2. *Excitatory state of primary sense organs*—The effect of accessory stimulation also depends on the initial degree of excitation of the sense organ undergoing primary stimulation. Thus, in order to increase the loudness of a tone on accessory visual stimulation, the initial loudness must be sufficiently great. Otherwise, either no effect with be demonstrable or a loss in loudness will occur.

3. *Duration of accessory stimulation*—As a rule, accessory effect becomes increasingly prominent during the first moments of accessory action, with a subsequent drop away from the maximum attained.

4. *Termination of accessory stimulation*—In evaluating the influence of accessory stimulation on a given sense organ, it is necessary to know whether the state of the organ was tested before or after cessation of accessory stimulation, since, after withdrawal of the accessory stimulus, the effect does not just wear off with an eventual return to normalcy. There frequently arises instead, a shift in an opposite direction to that of the initial effect. Lowered sensitivity may be followed by a supernormal phase, heightened sensitivity by a subnormal phase.

5. *Affectivity of stimulus*—It is not known how degree of liking influences response to dual stimuli. However, it has been claimed, for example, that gustatory and olfactory stimuli of unpleasant character cause a decline in peripheral sensitivity of the eye. It has also been reported that, after presentation of harmonious tones, color sensitivity of the dark-adapted eye to red and yellow was raised, to green-blue lowered, whereas disagreeable sounds reversed the effects.

6. *Physiological state*—The specific physiological state of the sense organs, as well as the more general physiological state of the individual, plays a role in sensory interaction. For example, it was demonstrated that with intense auditory stimulation, the electrical sensitivity of the

light-adapted eye underwent decrease, and that of the dark-adapted eye, increase.

7. *Diurnal variation*—The respective sensitivities of the rod and cone apparatus, for example, exhibited an inverse reciprocity of accessory influence that was diurnally dependent.

8. *Summation, repetition and cumulation of accessory effects*—If each of two sense modalities, on accessory stimulation, induces an increase in peripheral sensitivity of the eye, their joint action induces an effect beyond that induced singly. If, however, the individual effects are in opposite directions, their joint action induces a general effect on peripheral sensitivity equal approximately to their distance.

Constant repetition over equal intervals of time of the same accessory stimulus has been found frequently to yield a diminishing effect which tends to zero. Also, effects of accessory stimulation have been observed to linger, even from one day to the next.

Conclusions

It appears that all modalities undergo various modifications of sensory response on appropriate application of secondary stimulation. Where the primary stimulus is visual, the resulting modifications conform to predictable patterns, in many instances. Despite the large amount of Soviet experimentation, there exists a great need for further definitive studies. Quantification of individual variability in response to dual stimulation does not seem to have been investigated, nor has three-way stimulation been reported.

The results described in this presentation should be accepted with caution, as they are derived mainly from single, isolated experiments. With the advent of more sophistical tools and an increased interest in cross-disciplinary investigations, advances should soon be forthcoming in the complex area of sensory interaction.

References

[1] Sherrington, C. S., *Integrative Action of the Nervous System,* Yale University Press, New Haven, Conn., 1920.
[2] Parker, G. H. and Stabler, E. M., "On Certain Distinctions Between Taste and Smell," *American Journal of Physiology,* Vol. 32, 1913, pp. 230–240.
[3] Békésy, G. von, "Olfactory Analogue to Directional Hearing," *Journal of Applied Physiology,* Vol. 19, 1964, pp. 369–373.
[4] Mitchell, M. J., "Some Interrelationships of the Chemical Senses, Smell, Taste, and Irritance, at the Near-Threshold Level, and Trends Within the Series of *n*-Aliphatic Monohydric Alcohols," M.S. thesis, University of Canterbury, Christchurch, New Zealand, 1967, pp. 1–113.
[5] Börnstein, W. S., "Cortical Representation of Taste in Man and Monkey. I Functional and Anatomical Relations of Taste, Olfaction, and Somatic Sensibility," *Yale Journal of Biology and Medicine,* Vol. 12, 1940, pp. 719–736
[6] Benjamin, R. M., "Effect of Removal of Olfactory Bulbs on Taste Discrimination in Normal and Brain Operated Rats," *The Physiologist,* Vol. 3, No. 3, 1960, p. 19.

[7] Skramlik, E. von, *Handbuch der Physiologie der Niederensinne, Band 1: Der Physiologie des Geruchs und Geschmackssinnes,* Georg Thieme, Leipzig, 1926, pp. 1–532.

[8] Mackey, A. O. and Valassi, K., "The Discernment of Primary Tastes in the Presence of Different Food Textures," *Food Technology,* Vol. 10, 1956, pp. 238–240.

[9] Mackey, A., "Discernment of Taste Substances as Affected by Solvent Medium," *Food Research,* Vol. 23, 1958, pp. 580–583.

[10] Stone, H. and Oliver, S., "Effect of Viscosity on the Detection of Relative Sweetness Intensity of Sucrose Solutions," *Journal of Food Science,* Vol. 31, 1965, pp. 129–134.

[11] Moir, H. C., "Some Observations on the Appreciation of Flavour in Food-Stuffs," *Chemistry and Industry,* London, Vol. 55, 1936, pp. 145–148.

[12] Kanig, J. L., "Mental Impact of Colors in Food Studied," *Food Field Reporter,* Vol. 23, 1955, p. 57.

[13] Dunker, K., "The Influence of Past Experience Upon Perceptual Properties," *American Journal of Psychology,* Vol. 52, 1939, pp. 255–265.

[14] Hall, R. L., "Flavor Study Approaches at McCormick and Co., Inc.," *Flavor Research and Food Acceptance,* Arthur D. Little, Inc., ed., Reinhold, New York, 1958, pp. 224–240.

[15] Pangborn, R. M., "Influence of Color on the Discrimination of Sweetness," *American Journal of Psychology,* Vol. 73, 1960, pp. 229–238.

[16] Allen, F. and Schwartz, M., "The Effect of Stimulation of the Senses of Vision, Hearing, Taste, and Smell Upon the Sensibility of the Organs of Visions," *Journal of General Physiology,* Vol. 24, 1940, pp. 105–121.

[17] London, I. D., "Research on Sensory Interaction in the Soviet Union," *Psychological Bulletin,* Vol. 51, No. 6, 1954, pp. 531–568.

[18] Dobriakova, O. A., "Concerning the Parallel in Changes of Electrical Sensitivity of Organs of Vision and Taste Under the Influence of Optical and Taste Stimuli," *Fiziologicheskii Zhurnal,* SSSR, Vol. 26, 1939, pp. 192–198.

[19] Tronova, A. I., "Toward the Question of the Influence of Extraneous Stimuli on Change of Taste Sensitivity," *Trudy Instituta im. V. M. Bekhterova po Izucheniyu Mozga,* Vol. 13, 1940, pp. 175–182.

[20] Schutte, W. and Zubek, J. P., "Changes in Olfactory and Gustatory Sensitivity After Prolonged Visual Deprivation," *Canadian Journal of Psychology,* Vol. 21, no. 4, 1967, pp. 337–345.

[21] Gregson, R. A. M., "Modification of Perceived Relative Intensities of Acid Tastes by Ambient Illumination Changes," *Australian Journal of Psychology,* Vol. 16, 1964, pp. 190–199.

[22] Becker, B. and Morton, W. R., "Taste Sensitivity to Phenylthiourea in Glaucoma," *Science,* Vol. 144, No. 3624, 1964, pp. 1347–1348.

[23] Bernard, R. A., Halpern, B. P., and Kare, M. R., "Effect of Vitamin A Deficiency on Taste," *Proceedings of the Society for Experimental Biology and Medicine,* Vol. 108, 1962, pp. 784–786.

[24] Duncan, R. B. and Briggs, M., "Treatment of Uncomplicated Anosmia by Vitamin A," *Archives of Otolaryngology,* Vol. 75, 1962, pp. 116–124.

[25] Moulton, D. G., "Pigment and the Olfactory Mechanism," *Nature,* Vol. 195, 1962, pp. 1312–1313.

[29] Fauvelle, L. J., "Notes," *American Journal of Psychology,* Vol. 1, 1888, pp. CFTRI, India, Vol. 4, No. 6, 1955, p. 136.

[27] Pettit, L. A., "The Influence of Test Location and Accompanying Sound in Flavor Preference Testing of Tomato Juice," *Food Technology,* Vol. 12, 1958, pp. 55–57.

[28] Hoeven-Leonard, J. van der, "Riechscharfen- und Farbensinnabweichungen," *Umschau,* Vol. 12, 1908, pp. 367–369.

[29] Fauvelle, L. J., "Notes," *American Journal of Psychology* Vol. 1, 1888, pp. 357–358.

[30] Beidler, L. M., "Comparison of Gustatory Receptors, Olfactory Receptors,

and Free Nerve Endings," *Cold Spring Harbor Symposium on Quantitative Biology,* Vol. 30, 1965, pp. 191–200.

[*31*] Dawson, W., "Chemical Stimulation of the Peripheral Trigeminal Nerve," *Nature,* Vol. 196, 1962, pp. 341–345.

[*32*] Moulton, D. G., "Electrical Activity in the Olfactory System of Rabbits with Indwelling Electrodes," *Olfaction and Taste,* Y. Zotterman, ed., Macmillan, New York, 1963, pp. 71–84.

[*33*] Stone, H., Carregal, E. J., and Williams, B., "The Olfactory Trigeminal Response to Odorants," *Life Sciences,* Vol. 5, 1966, pp. 2195–2201.

[*34*] Hernández-Peón, R., Scherrer, H., and Jouvet, M., "Modification of Electric Activity in Cochlear Nucleus During 'Attention' in Unanesthetized Cats," *Science,* Vol. 123, 1956, pp. 331–332.

[*35*] Urbantschitsch, V., "Über den Einfluss einer Sinneserregung auf die übrigen Sinnesempfindungen," *Archives der Gesamten Physiologie,* Vol. 42, 1888.

[*36*] Lazarev, P. P., "The Influence of an Acoustic Stimulation Upon the Light Sensibility of the Eye," *Proceedings Academy of Science,* SSSR, Vol. 18A, 1927.

[*37*] Yakovlev, P. A., *Visual Sensations and Perceptions,* Moscow, Vol. 127, 1935 (cited by Allen and Schwartz, 1940).

[*38*] Kravkov, S. V., "The Influence of Sound Upon the Light and Color Sensibility of the Eye," *Acta Opthalmologica Scandinavica,* Vol. 14, 1936, pp. 348–360.

[*39*] Yakovlev, P. A., "The Influence of Acoustic Stimuli Upon the Limits of Visual Fields for Different Colors," *Journal of the Optical Society of America,* Vol. 28, 1938, pp. 286–289.

[*40*] Thompson, R. F., Voss, J. F., and Brogden, W. J., "Effect of Brightness of Simultaneous Visual Stimulation on Absolute Auditory Sensitivity," *Journal of Experimental Psychology,* Vol. 55, 1958, pp. 45–50.

[*41*] Dember, W. N., *The Psychology of Perception,* Holt, Rinehart and Winston, New York, 1963, pp. 221–224.

[*42*] Livanov, M. N., "On the Rhythmical Stimulation and Interrelations of the Fields of the Cerebral Cortex," *Fiziologicheskii Zhurnal SSSR,* Vol. 28, 1940, pp. 172–194.

[*43*] Walker, E. L. and Sawyer, T. M., Jr., "The Interaction Between Critical Flicker Frequency and Acoustic Stimulation," *Psychological Record,* Vol. 11, 1961, pp. 187–191.

[*44*] Small, A. M., Jr., "Audition," *Annual Review of Psychology,* Vol. 14, 1963, *pp.* 115–154.

[*45*] Rock, I. and Victor, J., "Vision and Touch: an Experimentally Created Conflict Between the Two Senses," *Science,* Vol. 143, No. 3606, 1964, pp. 594–596.

[*46*] Zinchenoko, V. P. and Ruzskaia, A. G., "Does Hand Teach Eye?" *Doklady Akademiia na Naukite RSFSR,* Vol. 3, 1962, pp. 87–90 (In: *Psych. Abstract.* Vol. 37, pp. 7870).

[*47*] Stellwagen, W. T. and Culbert, S. S., "Comparison of Blind and Sighted Subjects in the Discrimination of Texture," *Perceptual and Motor Skills,* Vol. 17, 1963, pp. 61–62.

[*48*] Axelrod, S., "Effects of Early Blindness: Performance of Blind and Sighted Children on Tactile and Auditory Tasks," *American Foundation for the Blind,* New York, 1959, pp. 1–83.

[*49*] Drake, B. K., "Food Crushing Sounds. An Introductory Study," *Journal of Food Science,* Vol. 28, 1963, pp. 233–241.

PART III: Principles and Techniques for Sensory Measurement and Analysis

Amihud Kramer[1]

Texture

REFERENCE: Kramer, Amihud, **"Texture,"** *Basic Principles of Sensory Evaluation, ASTM STP 433,* American Society for Testing and Materials, 1968, pp. 49–50.

Texture deals with the sense of feel and consequently the term "Kinesthetic," the muscle sense, has been used as a synonym. Another term closely related to the characteristic of texture is "tact," that is, the sense of touch. The adjective tactile refers to something perceptible to touch and tactual something produced by the sensation of touch.

Thus, any sensation that may affect the skin or the muscle endings may be considered within the framework of texture. Practically, however, the subject may be limited to hand, specifically finger feel, and mouth feel.

Mouth feel is at times considered part of the flavor area. It is suggested here that such attributes of mouth feel as chewiness, fibrousness, grittiness, mealiness, stickiness, oiliness, being essentially sensed by the muscular force applied in the process of mastication, be considered part of texture and only such sensations as heat, cold, or pain be included in the flavor category.

From the physical standpoint texture may be limited to that part of rheology that deals with the deformation or flow of matter, but only as a result of the application of forces greater than gravity. By this further restriction, we distinguish between texture and such terms as viscosity, which refers to the flow characteristics of Newtonian fluids, and consistency which refers to the flow characteristics of non-Newtonian liquids or semisolids. Texture, on the other hand, deals essentially with solids or solid gels.

Methods of Applying Force

Since forces greater than gravity are required to initiate flow there are five possible methods of applying such forces.

[1] Professor, College of Agriculture, Department of Agriculture, University of Maryland, College Park, Md.

1. *Deformation*—where the unit to which force is applied is changed in shape, but not divided.

2. *Compression*—where the force applied may reduce the volume of the object without dividing it.

3. *Tensile strength*—where the force is applied in such a way that the object is torn or pulled apart by forces applied away from the center of the object.

4. *Cutting force*—where the forces are applied in such a manner as to achieve the separation of an object into two or more parts without changing their shape. It is obvious that if a cutting operation were performed perfectly with no compression or other forms of force exerted, the cutting edge would have no width and the force required would be infinitesimal. Thus in practice a certain degree of compression, shearing, and perhaps even tensile force is involved with these so-called cutting operations, where the sharpness, thickness, and bevel of the cutting edge are of major importance and should be specified.

5. *Shearing force*—is defined as the force that causes two continuous parts of an object to slide relative to each other in a direction parallel to their plane of contact, so that we obtain both a separation in the object as in the case where cutting force is applied, and also a change in position. In practice it is practically impossible to obtain shearing without compression preceding the shear action. Thus with some preceding compression, shearing is perhaps the most common of the ordinary expressions of texture, essentially resembling the chewing action of the teeth.

Units of Measurement

Since textural measurement requires the application of force in one form or another, measurement may be in terms of pounds or grams of force exerted at a specific moment in time, this being usually at the point of maximum application of the force; or it could be in terms of work accomplished which would be the force used during the entire period in which the sample is tested. For such a measurement it would be necessary to chart a time-force curve and the integrated area under the curve would be equivalent to the work performed. To obtain the maximum use of force, a recorded curve would not be required, but a maximum dial indication would suffice. A recorded curve, in addition to having the advantage of making it possible to determine the total work performed, would also provide further information on the structural characteristics of the sample from the shape of the curve, and its slope.

E. T. Klemmer[1]

Psychological Principles of Subjective* Evaluation

REFERENCES: Klemmer, E. T., **"Psychological Principles of Subjective Evaluation,"** *Basic Principles of Sensory Evaluation, ASTM STP 433,* American Society for Testing and Materials, 1968, pp. 51–57.

The papers in this series on Physiology of the Senses describe the nature of man's receptors in terms of the ranges of stimulation to which they are sensitive and other key properties of these sensors. In addition to the characteristics of peripheral sense organs (such as sensory adaptation) which are important in assessing the results of subjective tests, there are many psychological factors of less obvious physiological basis which must be considered. The most significant and general of these psychological factors is the relevance of the judge's or observer's responses in the test situation for predicting the behavior of the ultimate consumer. Indeed, this is the very heart of the problem of subjective evaluation and is the first topic of the present section. There are also a large number of psychological factors which appear as extraneous or confounding effects. While not central to the test procedures, these may invalidate predictions made on the basis of subjective tests. A list of such confounding factors is given in the second part of this section, along with a definition of each.

In all, the purpose of the present section is to provide an overview of the fundamental questions to be faced in doing subjective testing. It is well to face these questions before becoming engrossed in the details of the testing procedures and statistical analysis of the data.

What Are We Measuring?

Typically in subjective evaluation we are concerned with the user's reaction to certain properties of a product, properties such as taste or

---

* The word "subjective" is used in the present paper to denote threshold, difference, preference, and acceptability tests both in the laboratory and in the field. The adjective "sensory" is often used in this regard, but it implies a limitation to the use of human observers as sensing devices rather than judging devices who use the sensory information as a data source for a decision process.

[1] Member of the technical staff, Bell Telephone Laboratories, Holmdel, N. J.

odor. This involves both measuring the pertinent physical properties and also measuring the user's reaction. We would really like to know the user's reaction in a natural-use setting, but it is often impossible to make measurements in such a setting. Even if some measurements could be made, they would likely not be reproducible in another natural setting because of failure to control extraneous environmental and personal factors, or simply because different criterion levels of suitability exist in different situations. The usual solution to this dilemma is to have judges or observers make evaluations under controlled conditions. It is assumed that there is an underlying psychological reaction to the product or stimulus in question, a reaction which occurs in both the controlled test and natural-use situations, and a reaction which governs the judge's response in the test and the user's reaction in the natural situation. Of course, predictions of customer behavior in the natural situation must consider the many other factors such as price, reputation of the manufacturer, supervisor's opinion, and personal relations with the supplier. The easiest way to eliminate the influence of these extraneous factors is to conduct the subjective evaluation tests away from the natural-use environment with judges who are not influenced by the extraneous factors. This may be accomplished either by using judges who are not familiar with the extraneous factors or by disguising the identity and price of the products.

Although these disguised factors are extraneous to subjective evaluation, they are essential to the decisions made in actual use. Therefore, it is seldom meaningful to ask the judges in a subjective evaluation test to make the same sort of practical decisions, for example: would you buy this product? Rather, the judges are asked to consider only their subjective evaluation to specific and immediate properties of the product (or even a simulated part of the product). The specification of properties of the product for the judges' attention and the method of analysis, of course, will depend upon the purpose of the test.

What are the purposes of laboratory subjective or sensory tests? One point of view regarding this question is that laboratory test panels are used solely to determine detectable differences and for measuring the amount of certain properties which cannot readily be measured by physical equipment, but that consumer surveys based on actual use of the product are required to determine preference or acceptance and that neither method can reasonably be used to do the task of the other.[2] Even such a separatist position does not completely avoid the assumption of a common basis of response between the sensory panel and the consumer, since the field test samples are presumably chosen on the basis of

    [2] Pangborn, R. M. and Dunkley, W. L., "Laboratory Procedures for Evaluating the Sensory Properties of Milk," *Dairy Science Abstracts,* Vol. 26, No. 2, 1964, pp. 55–62.

laboratory panel scaling. If all decisions about the acceptability of a new or changed product are made only on the basis of acceptance in actual use, then the only assumption that need be made is that the laboratory panel is judging the same basic variables with at least the same sensitivity as the ultimate consumer.

A broader point of view concerning the use of controlled laboratory methods of subjective tests would include predictions of product acceptability and preferences as well as the assignment of limits to the thresholds of detectable difference. The methods employed in testing, of course, will be different for the different applications. Thus, if the ultimate criterion is whether two bathroom tiles will be noticeably different in color, a different method would be required than to determine which color is preferred. Again, if it is desired to predict a point-of-sale decision by the customer, different methods would be used from those which try to predict customer satisfaction from continued use.

It is obvious, then, that subjective evaluation does not measure a single property with a fixed, one-dimensional subjective scale. For any product there are a large number of properties and scaling methods which can be involved. Some approaches produce more consistent results than others and some may correlate better with the ultimate criterion. In choosing the method one must consider both its consistency and predictive ability. In testing terms this is equivalent to considering both the reliability and validity of the instrument. As an example of this distinction, consider a test to assure that a product maintains its taste quality. Assume that a standard of quality can be formulated by the laboratory to be precisely the same each time it is made. Trained judges could then compare the factory product with the laboratory standard and make extremely consistent judgments about taste differences. The judgments might bear little relation, however, to what the ultimate consumer thought of the taste of the product. On the other hand a panel of representative consumers might be asked to judge the quality of the factory product. If user opinion is the ultimate criterion, this method might produce more valid answers than the first, even though the results were more variable. It must be kept in mind, however, that no method can have better predictive ability than consistency (high validity and poor reliability). Field testing with untrained judges under uncontrolled conditions will usually produce large variability in results and thus poor reliability. Low reliability can be overcome by taking large samples in such a way that the extraneous factors are not correlated with the experimental conditions. The requirement of large samples and random sampling methods is the price that must be paid for field testing.

In practice, it is not possible to avoid field testing entirely, since the ultimate criterion is one of actual use. Neither is it practical to do all subjective testing in the field, since the required volume of such tests would be prohibitive. One solution is to use laboratory tests to determine which properties are important and to set probable limits on the acceptability (or detectability) of each and then to use field tests to determine the optimum or permissible values of these properties for the actual users. Another solution is to have both the threshold studies and optimization studies done in a controlled laboratory setting with only periodic checks from field tests on the validity of the laboratory results. It is the thesis of the present paper that regardless of which approach is taken, it is essential to compare laboratory and field data to ascertain that the laboratory tests are indeed correlated, as assumed, with the reaction of actual users.

Possible Confounding Factors

Many psychological factors are present during subjective evaluation tests which often influence the results although they are not primary variables in the test. These will be given below in the form of a check list with a brief description or definition of each. Many of these items are covered in one or another of the other papers in this series. They are listed here to encourage consideration of these factors even before a specific method is chosen.

1. *Selection and training of judges*—It is important to face the question as to whether the judges should be highly trained experts or a representative sample of the ultimate users. If expert judges are used because of their reliability, then the validity of their judgments should be checked ultimately by using people representative of the class of normal purchasers or users. One fairly important exception to this rule is that those cases where a panel of expert judges fails to detect a difference, it is reasonable to assume that the average consumer or user will not detect a difference either. If the expert panel does detect differences, or if judgments of preference or acceptability are involved, then the validity checks with representative users are necessary.

2. *Interaction among judges*—If communication between judges is possible, their judgments may well be affected. This is particularly true if one of the judges is considered more senior or more experienced than another.

3. *Extraneous cues*—It is fairly obvious that extraneous cues which differentiate among the test items should not be present. For example, if taste is being evaluated, color, temperature, manufacturer, etc., should be equated or disguised.

4. *Coding symbols*—Preferential biases exist with regard to the choice of some symbols over others and some symbols have general connotations of order or rank. Three-digit random numbers are sometimes used to avoid these biases.

5. *Sequential effects*—If each judge makes more than one judgment

(as he typically does) then it is important to consider the influence of the order in which judgments are made and the time spacing between judgments. Ordinarily it is desirable to reduce sequential effects to a minimum by separating the judgments in time and counterbalancing the order or presentations. Special techniques to reduce sequential influence in taste and odor are described elsewhere.

The sequential effects may be due to successive contrast (improved discrimination between closely spaced stimuli), sensory adaptation (lowered sensitivity following stimulation), convergence effect (tendency to make similar responses to successive stimuli), time errors (bias in the judgment of a second stimulus as a function of the time of its presentation after the first stimulus), probability matching (tendency to make an expected number of judgments in each category), and the "gambler's fallacy" (tendency to change the judgment after a run of similar judgments).

A particular sequential effect of special importance is the marked effect upon the judge's opinion of one item due to the range of other items he is considering at the same time. For example, if preferences are sought for sugar concentration in a soft drink, the preferred level can be changed by changing the range of values used in the test, even though the preferred level always falls within the range tested.

A range effect also operates in discriminative testing and the scaling of sensory properties. In general, smaller ranges of stimuli will lead to greater precision in discrimination and expanded sensory scales. The effect is due to simultaneous and successive contrast between stimuli and the tendency for extreme values of stimuli to form better reference points or anchors than intermediate stimuli. The range effect can be partially avoided by using a paired comparison method. It can never be avoided completely, however, since it is part of the world in which we live. Subjective evaluations are sensitive to the range of alternatives offered.

6. *Motivational factors*—Subjectively based decisions may be influenced by factors such as cost, prestige, status, and other symbolism and associations produced by advertising. Even with the elimination of extraneous cues, such as product names, many motivational factors may still be associated with the product itself. If such do influence the judgments, then it is important to ascertain that the judges are influenced by these factors in a way similar to the ultimate users.

In addition to the attitudes that judges and users bring with them to any test there is the possibility of generalization of attitudes within the test itself. This is the well-known "halo-effect" in which a stimulus that is judged good (or poor) in one comparison tends to be judged the same way in other comparisons rather than being judged anew each time. The halo effect is thus both a motivational and sequential factor.

7. *Discriminability and value judgments*—Many of the methods used in the design and analysis of subjective tests utilize inconsistencies in the judges' responses as a basis for forming the subjective scale. But the responses may be based either upon an overall evaluation of the products along the appropriate subjective value dimension or a discrimination of a single physical difference between products plus a judgment as to the relation between this difference and the subjective value scale. The inconsistencies in judgment have very different implications for subjective differences in the two cases. For example, a 90 to 10 per cent division of judges' opinions with regard to the more natural of two voice transmission systems which differ only in noise level does not mean the same thing for difference in quality as a 90/10 split between samples which differ in distortion, bandwidth, noise, volume, peak clipping and echo.

Easily discriminable physical differences are very important in point-of-sale decisions (package design, product identification, product display), but if subjective scaling of more complex properties is being undertaken then care should be taken to avoid the possibility of the judge's decisions being based unduly on easily discriminable differences.[3]

8. *Learning effects*—Quite apart from the short-term sequential effects mentioned in Item 3 are long-term changes in the judge's response pattern due to the testing situation. If expert judges are used, it is hoped that any such change during a test will be small. If the judges are not experts, then the results may depend upon the length of the test or the number of different tests in which the judges participate. Counterbalancing order of presentation within a test will not eliminate these problems, although it will remove a bias in the results due to training *if all alternatives respond to training in a similar fashion*. Long-term changes can be detected by the use of control samples given several times in the testing procedure with disguised identification. For difference tests, learning effects appear as threshold shifts over successive time periods.

9. *Judge's criterion level*—Subjective tests generally assume a continuous function relating changes in the physical characteristics of the product and the subjective effect such changes have on the judge. The judge's response however is usually discrete. He may be only allowed "acceptable" and "not-acceptable" categories. Obviously, when this is done the test results will depend not only on the shape of the so-called psychophysical function relating physical stimulus and subjective effect, but also on how this function is divided into rating categories by the judge. The paired-comparison avoids this problem but suffers from the difficulty described in Item 3. Another solution is to provide "standard" stimuli, always the same, which define the borderline points on the psychophysical curve.

---

[3] Differences which are not easily discriminable to the layman may become discriminable to the expert judge through training.

10. *Attentional factors*—Although the human judge can make subjective evaluations of very complex things, at any moment only a few of the relevant variables are influential in his decision. For example, in judging the quality of printing, many identifiable variables are important (contrast, edge sharpness, voids, character alignment, splatter, etc.) but in comparing two samples perhaps only one of these variables may be controlling the decision. If the judge were somehow set to attend to another variable his decision could be different. The mechanism operates in the range effect and sequential effects listed above but may also be induced by other means. Indeed we may wish to modify the weighting of various factors in keeping with their relative importance in the situation of actual product use. On the other hand, if the influence of each elemental variable upon the criterion (dependent) variable can be accurately specified in advance, then a subjective test would not be necessary (except perhaps in those cases where sufficiently accurate instruments have not yet been developed to substitute for the human as a sensing device). For the most part, the subjective tests are necessary because it has not been possible to specify the interaction of the varying physical properties as they act together to produce an overall judgment on the part of the human. Thus, it would not be reasonable to attempt to instruct judges in any accurate way about the relative contribution that each elemental property should make to his judgment but some general guidelines about order of importance might be given.

11. *How well does the test predict the criterion of actual use?*—This question relates to the first part of the present section. It is placed here only as a reminder that the fundamental question of how well the overall method does its job should be faced early in the design of subjective evaluation and checked after the testing has been done. This must be done if the tests are to be operationally meaningful rather than unchecked expert opinion.

Acknowledgment

M. S. Schoeffler of the Bell Telephone Laboratories reviewed this paper and made helpful editorial suggestions and clarifications which have been incorporated in the manuscript. Several members of Subcommittee II of ASTM Committee E-18 made valuable suggestions about the content and analyses in the paper. In particular the contributions of R. M. Pangborn, N. F. Giradot, T. W. Lashof, H. Stone, and W. B. Knowles are acknowledged. The paper was revised in response to comments from these people, but this does not mean that they are in agreement with the particular points of view expressed herein.

D. H. Doehlert[1]

Methods for Measuring Degree of Subjective Response

REFERENCE: Doehlert, D. H., "**Methods for Measuring Degree of Subjective Response**," *Basic Principles of Sensory Evaluation, ASTM STP 433,* American Society for Testing and Materials, 1968, pp. 58–78.

Most data in engineering and science can be called objective data. That is, the data are obtained from physical instruments that measure characteristics of the phenomenon being observed. However, there are many instances for which it is necessary to rely upon the reactions of people rather than on the reactions of instruments. Such reactions are called *subjective responses.*

The following are examples of product characteristics which can be evaluated only by collecting subjective responses:

Softness of a pillow.

Drape of a fabric.

Uniformity of a film.

Luster of a yarn.

Streakiness of a fabric or film.

Taste or odor of a food product.

Appearance (style, design, decoration) of a product.

Many methods have been proposed for collecting and interpreting subjective responses. This monograph presents only those methods which are useful for measuring degree of response. These are the major methods of interest since interpolation is so often necessary. Limitations of time and money allow the experimenter to make only a few of the many possible variations of the product. And so he must predict by interpolation what the results would have been had the other variations been made. The methods described and evaluated here make interpolation possible when the responses are subjective.

[1] Consultant, Mathematics and Statistics Section, Engineering Dept., E. I. du Pont de Nemours & Co., Wilmington, Del.

Methods

Each method of interpreting and collecting subjective data has three parts:

1.) Pattern for presenting items to subjects.
2.) Question to pose to the subject and a form which the answers must take.
3.) Method of analysis.

In every method presented here the result of these three steps is a number for each item. This number is intended to represent the subjective response to the items. Obtaining such a number for each item is called *scaling the items*, and the numbers obtained are called *scale values*.

When the subjective responses have been assigned scale values by one of the methods of scaling, then it is possible to analyze these quantities just as objective data are analyzed.

One Item at a Time Methods

The four methods presented in this section require the subject to react to only one new item at a time. The simplicity of this task has advantages and disadvantages which will be mentioned.

Magnitude estimation—The method of magnitude estimation requires that the subject be presented one item at a time. The subject is asked to respond with a number proportional to his subjective response. The first item must be assigned an arbitrary number. This provides a scale unit. The first number can be assigned by the experimenter or by the subject. The subject is asked to associate this first number with the magnitude of his subjective response to the first item. Then he is asked, as he examines each subsequent item, to assign each a number proportional to his subjective response to the item in keeping with the number assigned to the first item. These numbers are called magnitude estimates.

Magnitude estimates measure degree of subjective response with no further analysis. When data from several people must be combined, the data from each person can be divided by the number for the first item in each set of data so that all persons will have a base point of 1.0.

A popular variation of magnitude estimation assigns arbitrary values to two items rather than one. This has the effect of making the zero on the scale of responses not meaningful. It does make the task somewhat easier since the subject is asked only for relative magnitudes instead of responses proportional to absolute magnitudes. Comments on the two base-points form of magnitude estimation apply equally to the one-base-point form. For more detail on magnitude estimation see Torgerson [1].[2]

---

[2] The italic numbers in brackets refer to the list of references appended to this paper.

Magnitude estimation is very fast and, on the face of it, very simple. Were it effective, there would be no need of other methods with other features.

However, it has been discovered that magnitude estimation is a very difficult task to require of subjects. It requires memory of the magnitude assigned to the previous item and the associated subjective reaction. If cumulative errors are to be avoided, the subjective reaction to the first item and the number assigned to it must be remembered. Probably because of failure to remember well, estimates for an item will shift when representations of an item are repeated among other items in a long sequence. The estimates are also affected by the magnitudes of the most recent subjective reactions to other items. Therefore, the estimates depend on the items just previously examined which is a bad situation.

Furthermore, ordinary subjects have some strange ideas about the real number line. Two items assigned numbers near ten and differing by one unit can have the same apparent difference to a subject as two items to which he has assigned numbers differing by several units in the thirties.

The method of ratio estimation described hereafter is an attempt to correct these deficiencies.

Ratio estimation—In ratio estimation the subject is presented with a pair of items and asked to report the ratio of his subjective responses.

When one particular item is always used as half of every pair then this is a one-item-at-a-time method since only one new item appears in each presentation. The analysis is just as simple as in magnitude estimation. An arbitrary number can be assigned to the item common to every pair. Every other item is assigned the product of that number and the reported ratio to the base item. These products measure the degree of subjective response.

This method is about as fast as magnitude estimation since the number of responses required of the subject is not different. It may be somewhat faster since the subject may be able to estimate ratio faster than he can estimate magnitude. This is a possibility because in ratio estimation both items are in front of him. In magnitude estimation he must remember previous items and their magnitude estimates.

The method of ratio estimation can be elaborated by showing the subject all possible pairs of items from the set being evaluated. This approach is a two-item-at-a-time method. The ratio reports obtained will not be perfectly compatible except perhaps as a very rare occurrence. Therefore, a method of analysis is necessary to resolve the conflicts. A method by Comrey to do this is available in Torgerson's book [1]. There is no advantage to showing all pairs yet it requires a complicated analysis.

The method of ratio estimation prevents the scale shifting that occurs in magnitude estimation, but it is still possible for the estimate to be affected by those estimates just previously reported. Some people tend toward the previous report; some feel obligated to report a variety of ratios almost without regard for the characteristics of the set of items. And again, as in magnitude estimation, requiring the subject to use numbers is inviting the peculiarities of his concepts of numbers to enter into the data.

Rating by standards—The problem of subjects using numbers and ratios in strange ways can be prevented by setting up a series of standards scattered over the range of the characteristic being evaluated. These can be assigned numbers by the experimenter and can serve as fixed points. Typically five to ten standard items will be selected and assigned the values 0, 1, 2, 3, . . . and so on. The standard items and their numbers together form a "rating scale."

The set of standards is kept near the subject. He is presented an item to rate and is asked to find the pair of standards which bracket his subjective reaction. Then he is asked to estimate a number between the two standards to represent the relative magnitude of his reaction.

This is again a fast method with no need for analysis. The numbers estimated can be used as they are as measures of degree of subjective response. The shifting of estimates by the subjects is limited to a small region by the presence of the fixed points on the scale. The more standards used, the more effectively the shifting is limited.

However, the flaw in this method lies in the arbitrary assignment of numerical values to the standards. This is likely to distort the scaling of subjective magnitude because the values for the standards are usually magnitude estimates provided rather arbitrarily by the experimenter. Therefore, rating suffers the deficiencies of magnitude estimation to that extent.

Furthermore, though one set of numbers for the standards may be all right for one subject, it is almost certain to have the wrong relationships for other subjects.

An example of interpolation of ratings is given by Hopkins [2].

Sorting into successive intervals—The method of sorting items into successive intervals (see Torgerson[1]) is quite similar to rating by standards. As in rating, a set of standard items are provided which are ordered by the experimenter from least to most of the characteristic being evaluated. The successive pairs of items in this series of standards form the successive intervals along the scale of the characteristic.

The use of successive intervals differs from rating in that numerical values are not assigned to the standard items and the subject is not required to give a number for each item. Instead, the subject is asked to place the item in one of the intervals such that his subjective response to the item is greater than his responses to standard items for lower intervals, and less than his responses to standard items for higher intervals.

For example, suppose three standard items are used, *A, B,* and *C,* where the experimenter states that $A < B < C$. Then suppose item x is to be evaluated. The subject must state $x < A$ or $A < x < B$ or $B < x < C$ or $C < x$. Sorting into successive intervals does not require interpolation within the intervals as does rating.

The analysis of the data obtained in this way is best presented after the section on Thurstone Scaling in which a similar and simpler analysis is given for a related type of data. We can say here that in the analysis of successive intervals data the standard items play the same role as the items sorted into the intervals. As a result numerical values are obtained both for the standard items and for the items being evaluated.

Paired Comparisons

The next five methods require the subject to react to two new items at a time. This would seem at first to be a more difficult task for the subject than a one-at-a-time approach. However, these methods require only a comparison of the two items presented. The subject does not have to remember previous responses and scoring systems; he does not have to refer to standard items. And so by simply asking for a comparison of the two items presented the task is actually simpler.

The comparison requested of the subject can be any comparison relevant to the experimenter's objective. The subject can be asked which is whiter, which is softer, which is tastier, which do you like better, or even which would you buy? Comparisons can sometimes be obtained without asking questions. For example, instead of asking which would you buy, the pair of items could be displayed in a store side-by-side where any customer seeing one would see the other. Then each sale would be a paired comparison favoring the one purchased.

In the discussion of paired comparisons which follows we will say that the outcome of comparing items i and j is either "i is greater than j" or "j is greater than i." The word "greater" is merely our convention and represents "whiter" or "liked better" or "softer" or "tastier" as the case may be.

The advantage of a paired comparison is its freedom from dependence on scoring systems, memory, and previous subjective responses. The price that must be paid for this advantage is increased complexity of analysis. The comparisons themselves do not produce numbers ready for interpolation. Rather, the comparisons must be converted by some form of analysis to numerical scale values for the items. Then these scale values can be used for interpolation.

The five methods presented here are therefore methods for analyzing paired comparisons.

A paired comparison produces one result for each pair of items. In this section we will consider only sets of data in which all possible pairs are represented equally often. Such sets of data are called balanced paired comparisons.

For t items where are $t(t - 1)/2$ possible pairs. For regression we must have one scale value per item, that is, t scale values. Analysis of paired comparisons then is a problem of reducing $t(t - 1)/2$ comparisons to t scale values.

Bradley-Terry model and analysis—Bradley and Terry [3] assume that for every pair of items i and j there is a probability, π_{ij} that i will be identified as greater. There are $t(t - 1)/2$ such π_{ij} values, one for each pair. If ties are not allowed the probability that j will be greater is $\pi_{ji} = 1 - \pi_{ij}$. Ties are discussed in Gridgeman [4], in Howorth and Oliver [5] and in Glenn and David [6]. For interpolation problems ties should not be allowed. However, analyses allowing ties will be noted where they are available.

They then hypothesize t scale values which are conveniently labeled $\log \pi_i$. The problem is to estimate the $\log \pi_i$ values from the comparison data. To do this Bradley and Terry suggest the model $\pi_{ij} = \pi_i/(\pi_i + \pi_j)$. Using this model they obtain maximum likelihood estimates for the π_i. Tables of these estimates are available in their paper and another by Bradley [7] for small numbers of items and replications. Approximations are available for larger numbers of items [8]. Tests of fit and other details are presented by Bradley [9,10]. Luce [11] has shown that for certain assumptions the scale values form a ratio scaling, that is, the zero is meaningful.

The basic assumption of the Bradley-Terry model is that a paired comparison is probabilistic, that is, for a pair the comparison will not always favor the same item. This is supported by experience. A pair of items can be shown to a subject again and again allowing time intervals to prevent the subject from recalling previous comparisons. The result will not always be the same if the difference is small. This is the situation relevant to the Bradley-Terry model, that is, small differences between items so that π_{ij} is less than one and greater than zero.

If for one or more pairs the difference between items is very large then π_{ij} is one or zero. This can readily happen. A simple example will demonstrate that this possibility is quite realistic. Two cups of water differing by only a few drops will not be clearly different in subjective weight. As pairs of cups differing by larger amounts are compared there will come a difference which is so large that it will always be reported one way. For example, a full cup will always be reported heavier than a quarter cup.

This type of difference, call it an "always-noticeable difference," presents problems for the Bradley-Terry model. The model can tolerate several such pairs provided the set of items cannot be divided into two subsets such that every item in one set always comes out greater than every item in the other subset. When the items can be divided this way the scaling problem must be separated into two problems, one for each subset of items. The analysis can estimate scale values for each subset but no estimate can be obtained of the separation of the two sets on that scale.

It is also possible that items can be so nearly alike that the subject cannot possibly detect a difference. In the example the two cups of water differing by a few drops can be presented over and over again with different labeling to disguise the difference in weight. It is possible that no matter how many comparisons are made the per cent of responses correctly picking the cup with more water will never be significantly different from chance (50 per cent). When this is so, the items have a "never-noticeable-difference." The Bradley-Terry model assumes that never-noticeable-differences do not occur.

However, these two shortcomings are not usually serious. In practice the differences will usually be neither too large nor too small. A small percentage of always-noticeable-differences and never-noticeable-differences will cause little difficulty.

The Bradley-Terry model has been used successfully. For small numbers of items (up to 10 or 15) it is usually not too difficult to make all paired comparisons. For 15 items there are 105 comparisons; for 20 items, there are 190 comparisons. It should be recognized that the Bradley-Terry model (and the four methods that follow) require that every comparison be made, and made equally often. Therefore, when large numbers of items must be scaled, as will be the case in interpolation problems, these methods become cumbersome. The large number of comparisons can take a long time. This time can be reduced somewhat by presenting more than two items at a time, an approach which will be discussed later.

The aforementioned analysis applies to data in which all pairs have been compared equally often. Ford [12] has provided an iterative solution for the π_i scale values when pairs have not been compared equally often though he does not list the Bradley papers in his references. In fact, some pairs may not have been compared at all. The method is based on maximum likelihood as is the Bradley-Terry analysis. Dykstra [13] later presented the same iterative procedure apparently unaware of the paper by Ford. Dykstra also presents in that paper a review of designs in which some pairs are left out altogether but other pairs are replicated equally often. However, the effect of lack of balance on the estimates is not known. Therefore, it is preferable to have completely balanced data. If the task of making comparisons of all pairs is too much for one subject, then designs by Bose [14], David [15], and Kendall [16] can be used in which each judge sees fewer than the total set of pairs. In these designs the combined data for all judges include every pair an equal number of times. Wilkinson [17] provides for these designs a series of tests of the judges and the π_i values based on the Bradley-Terry model and gives an example.

Thurstone scaling—The Thurstone analysis of paired comparisons is based on assumptions which are rather different from those made by Bradley and Terry. The normal distribution is introduced by Thurstone and this makes estimation rather easy.

Thurstone [18] assumed that each item gives rise to a response r_i in the individual; that these responses differ only quantitatively from one another; and that an item does not produce exactly the same response every time it is seen by the subject, but, rather, responses to an item are distributed around a mean. He assumed a normal distribution for each item-response with zero correlations between responses.

Under these assumptions the difference of two responses will also be normally distributed. A subject, when shown a pair, say items k and j, will report i greater than j when $r_i > r_j$, that is, when the difference between his two responses $(r_i - r_j)$ is greater than 0.

The scale unit for estimates of the r_i can be set equal to the standard deviation assumed common to all the responses. Then the frequency of reporting the item i greater than item j is the area of the normal curve (with unit variance) above the value $-(r_i - r_j)$. These frequencies are the observable quantities. Therefore the first step in analysis consists of finding the normal deviate such that the area of the normal distribution between the deviate and infinity is the observed proportion of statements, "$i > j$" when i and j are compared.

These normal deviates are estimates of $-(r_i - r_j)$ for all i, j pairs. Then by adding over j all estimates involving i and dividing by the number of items, t, an estimate of the response r_i is obtained. This technique arbitrarily sets the average of the estimates equal to zero. Estimating with an arbitrary zero is called interval scaling; that is, the zero is not meaningful. The estimated responses, r_i can then be used as measurements of degree of subjective response.

Details of the estimation procedure are given by Jackson and Fleckenstein [19], and by Mosteller [20,21] who showed that it is a least squares procedure. He also showed that Thurstone's requirement of zero correlations between responses is unnecessarily strict. The method requires only that correlations be equal. He also gives a test of fit.

In its original form this model could not deal with the problem of always-noticeable-differences which is mentioned earlier. If an item i is always reported greater than item j, then $(r_i - r_j)$ must be estimated equal to infinity. This is the result of the method even if the difference is actually less than always-noticeable. This result upsets the estimation of the r_i's. However, Morrissey [22], and independently Gulliksen [23], showed a least squares solution which omits the item pairs which were reported all one way (that is, always $i > j$ or always $j > i$). In this modification much of the ease of computation, which is the advantage in the Thurstone method, is lost. Computation is not so easy because a matrix of $(\frac{1}{2})t(t - 1) - q + 1$ rows must be prepared where t is the number of items and q is the number of pairs always reported one way. As t increases this number increases rapidly provided q is small. A large q would mean setting aside much data. Rather than set aside a large portion of the data, a method should be selected which does not suffer from this problem. Even for small q (less than 10 per cent of the pairs) and for large t that occur in practice (say 10 or more) the method becomes cumbersome (40 rows or more in the matrix).

There is no assurance before collecting the data that t and q will have a satisfactory relationship, unless by prior knowledge one can say that the items are very much alike (small q). Therefore, a method which would not require this prior information would be preferred.

Bradley has pointed out that the scale values for the items obtained by the Thurstone analysis are about the same as the scale values, log π_i , by the Bradley-Terry method. This is based on the fact that the integral of the normal curve and the integral of the hyperbolic secant are nearly identical. This is shown in Torgerson [1] and earlier in Gridgeman [24] and in Maxwell [25].

The Thurstone method has been used a great deal especially in psychological work where the item set can be altered freely. When an always-noticeable-difference or a never-noticeable-difference occurs, one of the items in the pair can be dropped or additional items can be added to the set having scale values between the two in the pair. In this way a set of data can be obtained which is free from pairs reported always one way, and free of undetectable differences. However, in industrial situations the item set is likely to be fixed. Adding items will probably be impossible in the time available and discarding items, wasteful. Therefore, methods free of this limitation will be preferred.

Glenn and David [6] have extended the Thurstone analysis to cover cases in which the possibility of never-noticeable-differences is admitted. In this situation ties would be allowed. Their analysis obtains estimates by least squares of the minimum detectable difference (threshold) and the item scale values. In place of Thurstone's assumption of a normal distribution of item differences they use an angular response law in order to overcome difficulties due to correlations.

It is appropriate at this point to discuss the analysis of results of sorting items into successive intervals. The method of data collection by successive intervals was introduced earlier, but discussion of the analysis of the resulting data was postponed until after the Thurstone analysis discussed above.

The Thurstone analysis applies to paired comparisons. So to see its application to successive intervals data we should recognize the paired comparisons implicit in placing an item in an interval. First we notice that an item placed in an interval is automatically evaluated greater than any item placed in a lower interval. Also it is evaluated less than items placed in higher intervals. Next we notice that an item placed in an interval is thereby evaluated greater than the items (or words) representing the boundaries of lower intervals. And likewise it is rated less than the boundaries of higher intervals.

These are paired comparisons. They involve not only the items being evaluated but also the boundaries of the intervals. These boundaries can be considered items for the sake of analysis. Therefore istead of t items we have $(t + s)$ items where s is the number of interval boundaries.

These paired comparisons implicit in successive intervals data do not include all possible paired comparisons. Any pair of items, both placed in the same interval, is a pair for which no comparison is made by the subject. Therefore, successive intervals data can be understood as paired comparison data for which data on some pairs are missing. The missing data analysis of Morrissey and Gulliksen, described above, can be applied.

When we prepare to analyze successive intervals data by the Morrissey-Gulliksen method we find that the list of pairs which can be analyzed is diminished for two reasons. First, to accomplish the purpose of their analysis we must drop those pairs where the data favors one item in the pair over the other in every comparison of the two. Then because successive intervals have been used we find that many paired comparisons have not been made. These two types of missing pairs will not overlap much, if at all. This is because the first kind of pair has a large difference (comparison always favors one of the items). The second kind of pair has a small difference (both items in the pair fall in the same interval).

This suggests that in any particular case we will find that too many pairs are missing to use this approach. There are steps that can be taken to avoid this difficulty to some extent. First, we can use many successive intervals to cover the range of interest. Then each interval will contain fewer items and thereby fewer pairs are left uncompared. Second, we can test only those groups of items with few if any always-noticeable-differences. But we should recognize that the experimenter might not have this option.

When looked at this way successive intervals can be seen as a very good way to speed up paired comparisons. In fact a complete set of paired comparisons can be obtained rather quickly by making a first pass using successive intervals and then asking the subject to make all paired comparisons within the group he has placed in each interval. This gives a complete set of paired comparisons which can then be analyzed by any of the four methods in the section on Paired Comparisons. Without this extension the method can produce data which might not be worth analysis.

Bradley et al [26] report that results which they have obtained from the analysis above have been "rather meaningless in that scores obtained for scale points did not at all match the order suggested by verbal, or otherwise indicated, orders on the scales." To avoid this difficulty they have developed an iterative procedure for finding scale values for the standard or boundary points. Their estimates maximize the item differences relative to within item variation. They have prepared a computer program for the IBM 650 computer to obtain these estimates. Some properties of these estimates have been investigated while others have not. In the same paper they discuss the problem of the number of standards to use in a successive intervals procedure.

Rankits—Bliss [27] has suggested an analysis which employs the Thurstone model but which uses a different estimation procedure. As in the Thurstone model, each item is assumed to produce a sensation distributed normally about its mean, μ_i. Therefore, a pair of items produces a pair of sensations with a difference that is distributed normally about the difference between the means, $(\mu_i - \mu_j)$. This normal distribution is assumed to apply to replications of comparisons of two items by the same subject. This can be extended to apply to comparisons by many subjects if the subjects can be assumed to have the same mean difference of sensations and the same variance.

The data produced in either case are n_i comparisons stating item i greater and n_j comparisons stating j greater. Bliss has suggested a method of estimating $(\mu_i - \mu_j)$ from n_i and n_j. Estimates of the μ_i scale values would then be obtained as in the Thurstone analysis by averaging all estimates of $(\mu_i - \mu_j)$ for $j = 1$ to t items.

The Bliss method of estimating $(\mu_i - \mu_j)$ is developed from the fact that if the model is applicable, then all n_i comparisons arise from comparisons where the sensation, r_i, was actually greater than the sensation, r_j. Similarly for all n_j comparisons r_j was actually greater than r_i. This implies that in the distribution of observed $(r_i - r_j)$ values about the mean $(\mu_i - \mu_j)$ the zero point is located such that in the sample of n responses n_i lie above zero and n_j lie below zero. This further implies that in an ordering of the responses, $(r_i - r_j)$ least to greatest the n_i value of $(r_i - r_j)$ is nearer the zero point $(r_i = r_j)$ than all other negative values of $(r_i - r_j)$. And the $(n_j + 1)$st response is nearer zero than all other positive values of $(r_i - r_j)$. If estimates of these two values can be obtained, then the deviation of the zero point from the mean $(\mu_i - \mu_j)$ can be estimated. The negative of that deviation is then the estimate of $(\mu_i - \mu_j)$.

The n_jth value in an ordered set of n random normal deviates has an expected value which has been tabled by Fisher and Yates [28]. In fact the expected values of all the ordered deviates in samples of n for $n = 2(1)$ 50 are given in that table. These expected values are called rankits. The argument in the paragraph above claims that the deviation of the zero point from $(\mu_i - \mu_j)$ lies between the n_jth rankit and the $(n_j + 1)$st rankit. Bliss suggested that the n_jth rankit be used without interpolation. If this is done for all possible pairs, in both orders then each item in a pair will appear once as the ith item and once as the jth item. Then averaging for estimating μ_i will have the effect of averaging the n_jth and the $(n_j + 1)$st rankits. Thus the method actually uses linear interpolation between rankits (by averaging) though this is not explicit in the paper by Bliss.

There is nothing in this method to make it preferable to the Thurstone analysis. The Thurstone method estimates the normal deviate of the zero point directly from a table of areas under the normal curve using $n_j/(n_i + n_j)$ as the observed proportion or area to the left of zero. The Bliss method estimates two points either side of zero: the jth and $(i + 1)$st rankits and then interpolates the zero point. The Bliss method seems unnecessarily complicated.

Row sums—The simplest estimates of scale values from balanced paired comparisons are row sums. The name "row sums" arises from the practice of arranging paired comparison data in a preference matrix. "Comparison" could have been used in place of "preference" since a preference is one type of comparison. A matrix is convenient because the results of comparisons involving say the ith item can be entered in the ith row and ith column. When the ith item is greater than the jth item a one is entered in the ij cell of the matrix and a zero in the ji cell.

For example, if four items are compared in pairs the results could be as follows: $A > B$, $A > C$, $C > B$, $D > A$, $D > B$, and $D > C$. A preference matrix for these data would have four rows and four columns as below. The comparison $A > B$ would be entered as a 1 in the A-row-B-column cell and an 0 in the BA cell. Thus, for the six pairs there are six ones and six zeros entered. The diagonal cells are meaningless as no item is compared with itself.

	A	B	C	D
A		1	1	0
B	0		0	0
C	0	1		0
D	1	1	1	

The row sums are the totals for the rows; in this case 2, 0, 1, 3. Thus the row sum for an item is the number of times it has been preferred over other items. It is rather obvious that paired comparisons must be balanced if row sums are to be used. For if the same item were compared with fewer than all the others its row sum would tend to be low. The fewer comparisons involving the item, the lower would be the row sum. But when all pairs have been compared, the row sum is not dependent on a pattern of comparisons that could be different from item to item.

The row sums can be used as a measure of degree of subjective response. It is instructive to compare row sums with rating by a set of standards. For the sake of comparison let us assume that we have five standards which have been assigned the numbers 1, 2, 3, 4, and 5. Call these standards S_1, S_2, S_3, S_4, and S_5. We will assume that $S_5 > S_4 > S_3 > S_2 > S_1$. Let us also assume in this example that we will not ask the subjects to interpolate. That is, an item preferred over S_4 but not preferred over S_5 will be given the scale value 4.0.

Now consider one item from the set of items that is to be scaled. Let us say that it receives a scale value estimate of 4 from comparison with the standards. Suppose now that we were to make paired comparisons of it with each of the five standards. If one point is given to this item each time it is preferred over some other then it will receive a total score of four since it is greater than S_1, S_2, S_3, and S_4. Therefore, the procedure of giving an item one point each time it is preferred over a standard is actually quite similar to the method of row sums. The difference is that in row sums the comparisons are not made against a set of standards. Rather, each experimental item is compared with the $t - 1$ other experimental items. Thus, row sums are similar to ratings against a standard set except that in row sums the items are not compared with a strictly standard set.

Baseball standings at the end of the season are examples of row sums. The row sums are the numbers of wins and the standings are obtained simply by division by the total number of games played, a constant for all teams. Each team is compared with a different set of teams, namely, the league without themselves.

We can see, therefore, that even if every item has been compared an equal number of times with every other item, there is still a lack of balance in that the opposition, so to speak, of every item is different. The properties of row sums as scale values have not been investigated. However, row sums are frequently used as scale values. The computation required is very slight. The assumptions involved in using row sums have not been properly identified. Only part of the difficulty is avoided if all items are compared to a standard set. Some pairs will have large differences, some small differences, yet row sums will count these comparisons equally.

Powering—Powering is an analysis of paired comparisons which is an extension of row sums. In the section above it was pointed out that a row sum is a count of the number of times that an item is greater than the

$t - 1$ other items in the set. In this count each comparison is given equal weight yet in some cases the difference is greater than in others.

The method of powering the preference matrix suggested by Wei [29] and Kendall [16] is designed to take into account the degrees of difference between items which are ignored in forming row sums. The degree of difference can be approximated by the difference between row sums. Therefore, the first step of analysis by powering is to form new scale values where each comparison is weighted by the associated row sum. Using the preference matrix defined above this procedure is merely premultiplication of the column vector of row sums by the preference matrix. (Diagonal cells can be given any value provided all diagonal cells are given the same value.)

This creates new scale values which can have different relationships, even a different rank order from the row sums. Kendall suggests that in some problems the new rank order may be theoretically preferable. It is only a short step to wonder if the new scale values can be considered an improvement over the row sums. There is no theory to serve as a guide here. It is possible that in some problems these new scale values might be the most appropriate scale values for the items.

The method can be extended by repeating the matrix multiplication again and again using the new scale values as the new column vector for each succeeding step. Using the method as described above the scale values will increase at each step making it difficult to determine whether or not the scale values are approaching stable relative values. However, by a simple device the results at successive steps can be compared. By adding a row of ones at the bottom of the matrix (and a corresponding column of zeros) and by adding the row sum for that row (which will be t), we will have added an artificial item which has the maximum possible score. After every multiplication we can divide the scale values by the last value which is the maximum possible. Therefore, all of the resulting relative values will be between 0 and 1. In practice these relative values appear to converge rather rapidly to limiting values. The limiting values are perhaps the appropriate values for use in a regression analysis of the items.

This method is called powering because raising the preference matrix to the pth power and then taking row sums gives exactly the same results as p matrix-multiplications as defined above.

Examples of powering and additional details can be found in Ref 30.

Rating of Differences

In this method items are presented two at a time as in the section on Paired Comparisons. However, the subject is asked to rate the difference between the two items in the pair. Rating of single items is discussed earlier. Rating of differences introduces a few complications.

To rate the difference between two items the subject must be supplied with a rating scale. If we wished to parallel the rating of single items we would supply a set of pairs showing several degrees of difference and we would associate a number with each degree of difference represented. This is not usually done. Rather the experimenter usually asks: Is the difference strong, moderate, or slight? Other words can be used. More or fewer words to represent more or fewer degrees of difference can be used. To obtain numerical scale values the numbers 3, 2, and 1 are usually associated with strong, moderate, or slight. Thus, the difference between items i and j can be rated as follows:

+3 if i is greater and the difference is strong
+2 if i is greater and the difference is moderate
+1 if i is greater and the difference is slight
 0 if there is no difference
−1 if j is greater and the difference is slight
−2 if j is greater and the difference is moderate
−3 if j is greater and the difference is strong

Scheffe [31] has developed an analysis of variance for data of this type. His analysis makes possible conclusions about the differences between subjects and the effects of order of presentation as well as conclusions about the items. For the interpolation problem we are only interested in the aspect of his analysis which produces scale values for the items. The scale value for an item is obtained in his analysis by averaging all the scores for pairs in which that item appears. For those pairs where the item was stated greater by the subject the score will be +3, +2, or +1. For those pairs where the item was the lesser the score will by −3, −2, or −1. Where the subject indicated no difference the score will be 0. For balanced data every item will appear in a pair with every other item. For t items then there will be $(t-1)$ scores to average.

This method is quite similar to Thurstone's procedure. Here the size of the difference between two items is estimated and reported by the subject. In the Thurstone analysis the size of the difference was obtained by observing a frequency of reports of one item greater than the other and converting this to a measure of the difference by means of the normal distribution assumption. Thus, in the rating of differences, only one presentation of each pair is necessary. In the Thurstone method repeated presentations must be made either to the same subject over and over or to many subjects who can be assumed to be reacting similarly.

However, the rating of differences is a more difficult task for the subject than a single paired-comparison. Experience has shown that as the task for the subject is made more difficult the responses become unstable. For example, a difference rated strong positive under some circumstances could be rated moderate positive under other circumstances. Had paired comparisons been used in both situations the result would be consistent since the same item is greater both times. Therefore rating of pairs invites instability via the changing interpretation of the words.

A second criticism of rating differences is the arbitrary nature of the numbers assigned to the words. Instead of 1, 2, and 3 for slight, moderate, and strong we might just as well have used 0.8, 1.2, and 3.0. Any three numbers increasing in magnitude could be used. We have no basis for selecting one set of numbers. Furthermore, a set of numbers appropriate for one person may well be inappropriate for another person. Subjects cannot be expected to have a uniform interpretation of words such as slight, moderate, and strong.

Despite these difficulties the method has served satisfactorily in some problems. An example has been published by Fleckenstein et al [32].

TABLE 1—*Combinations possible.*

Number of items	3	4	5	6	7	8	9	10	20	30
Number of possible pairs	3	6	10	15	21	28	36	45	190	435
Number of possible triples	1	4	10	20	35	56	84	120	1140	4060

TABLE 2—*Combinations necessary to get all possible pairs.*

Number of items	6	7	9	10	13	15	19	21
Number of pairs possible	15	21	36	45	78	105	171	210
Number of triples necessary	10	7	12	30	36	35	57	70

Three or More Items at a Time

Ranking in groups of three or more can be used to reduce the time and effort required for evaluation. When the number of items is large the number of possible pairs becomes very large. Most analyses require that all pairs be evaluated. Therefore, when large numbers of items are to be evaluated together, some other method than paired comparisons must be found for the presentation of the items if excessive evaluation is to be avoided.

Ranking in groups of three or more can produce paired comparison data. For example, a ranking of B > A > C can be restated as three paired comparisons: B > A; B > C; A > C. Some pair-wise interrelationships automatically become impossible when paired comparisons are obtained from rankings of three or more. For example, when the subject ranks A, B, and C the following pairwise relationship cannot occur: A > B; A > C; C > B. The requirement of a ranking has excluded this relationship which is called a circular triad. This restriction is usually of no consequence but should be recognized. More detail on circular triads is provided by this author [30].

If it were necessary to rank all possible triples, then there would be no advantage for triples when the number of items is large. This is shown in Table 1.

However, it is not necessary to rank all possible triples to get data on all possible pairs. Plans of triples which include all possible pairs are called balanced incomplete block designs of block size 3. These plans are available in Cochran and Cox [33] and in Kitagawa [34] for the cases listed in Table 2. In this table the columns show for various items the number of triples necessary to include all the possible pairs.

For six and ten items the triples listed in the plan include each pair twice. In every other case the triples include each pair only once. Durbin [35] gives a simple example using seven triples to compare seven items. Cochran and Cox discuss balanced incomplete blocks in taste and preference testing on p. 440 of the second edition of *Experimental Designs* [33].

It is apparent that where the plans are available the savings in the number of presentations will be one third or two thirds. The question of whether or not the subject can rank three items as fast, can be answered only by experiment. Experience usually shows that triples do not take half again as much time as pairs. Therefore, these incomplete block designs are usually improvements in efficiency over paired comparisons.

It is interesting to notice that if the number of items to be evaluated does not appear in Table 2, it may still be possible to avoid making all paired comparisons by adding extra items until the total number of items can be found in the table. For example, eleven items require 55 pairs. But by adding two additional items the design for 13 items can be used which requires only 26 triples. In fact, the requirement for 13 items (26 triples) is less than the requirement for ten items (30 triples). However, the ten-item design gives duplicates for every pair, an attractive aspect of the plan which is not available in the 13 item design.

Items can be ranked in groups of 4, 5, or more. Incomplete block designs similar to those for blocks of 3 can be found for some numbers of items per block greater than 3. The upper limit on the group size will be determined only by the experimental situation. For example, in taste testing the problems of lingering taste and satiation often put on an upper limit of two items at a time. That is, three items or more at a time are too many for the subject. Also, where very large items are being evaluated such as large pieces of carpets, it may be necessary to rank in groups of no more than two or three. Otherwise too much space is needed and too much walking is required of a subject.

For all of the aforementioned plans the analysis can be done by converting the rankings to paired comparisons and then analyzing by one of the methods described earlier. There two additional methods of analysis below that apply specifically to evaluation in blocks of more than two items.

Rating in incomplete blocks—Calvin [36] has observed that when magnitude estimation is used for incomplete blocks of items the scores within a block are often correlated. The ratings of items not very different tend to get spread out. Items quite different get ratings more nearly alike when in the same block. Calvin has provided a model in which there is a term, α_{ij}, for the correlation effect common to the ith and jth items when they are in the same block. These α_{ij} parameters represent the dependence of the rating of the ith item on the presence of the jth item.

The analysis of incomplete block designs is simplified if each pair of items appears in blocks an equal number of times, λ. Designs filling this requirement are called "balanced" incomplete block designs. Calvin shows that the estimation of the α_{ij} parameters is simplified if a similar requirement is placed on triples, that is, if each set of three items appears in blocks an equal number of times, δ. When both λ and δ are constant for all pairs and triples respectively then the design is called "doubly balanced." He gives the details of analysis, an example, and discusses construction of doubly balanced incomplete block designs. He notes that the precision of the estimates of the α_{ij} is proportional to $(\lambda - \delta)$. He further shows that $(\lambda - \delta)$ is larger for smaller block sizes. This would indicate greatest precision for block sizes of two, which are paired comparisons. However, he points out that this reasoning assumes the α_{ij} are the same for all block sizes. The α_{ij} may actually decrease with increasing block size so that larger blocks may be more efficient.

Most incomplete block designs catalogued in references already listed are not doubly balanced. Calvin gives methods for constructing doubly balanced designs and provides six designs for 8, 10, 12, and 16 items.

Bradley-Terry model for triple comparisons—The Bradley-Terry Model has been extended to the case of triple comparisons. In this extended model the probability that the items are ranked in the i, j, k order is:

$$\pi_i^2 - \pi_j/\Delta_{ijk} \quad \text{where} \quad \Delta_{ijk} = \pi_i^2(\pi_j + {}_k) + \pi_j^2(\pi_i + \pi_k) + \pi_k^2(\pi_i + \pi_j).$$

If this analysis is used then the $\ln \pi_i$ can again serve as scale values The complete analysis and examples are given by Pendergrass and Bradley [37] and Park [38]. Park compares triple comparison with paired comparison and concludes that triples do not introduce significantly more fatigue than pairs. However, he warns that when the items differ in more than just one characteristic, then the triple comparison approach is more vulnerable to complications than is paired comparison.

Recommendations

In the section on Paired Comparisons a dozen different procedures for obtaining subjective scale values were discussed. For each procedure there is a situation in which it is the best procedure to use. However, the following suggestions will cover almost all situations:

Use Rating Scales

(a) When a large number of items must be evaluated.

(b) When the characteristic is specified and easily understood.

(c) When the subjects have been well trained in evaluating the characteristic.

To be most effective the number of scale points should be determined by a preliminary measurement of the variability of the raters. The numbers for the standards should be obtained by some scaling procedure such as successive intervals.

Use Successive Intervals

(a) When the evaluators have not been trained.

(b) But the characteristic is specific and easily understood.

The procedure will be improved if sorting into intervals is followed by ranking of the items falling in the same interval.

Use Ranking

When the characteristic is not specific such as preference and appearance.

When ranking use balanced incomplete blocks for sets of items too large to rank as a complete set. The block size should be chosen for rapid and comfortable evaluation:

(a) Blocks of two or three for taste and odor tests.

(b) Blocks of three to five for tactile tests.

(c) Blocks of four to twelve for visual tests.

References

[1] Torgerson, W., *Theory and Methods of Scaling,* Wiley, New York, 1958.

[2] Hopkins, J. W., "A Procedure for Quantifying Subjective Appraisals of Odor, Flavor and Texture of Foodstuffs," *Biometrics,* Vol. 6, 1950, pp. 1–16.

[3] Bradley, R. A. and Terry, M. E., "Rank Analysis of Incomplete Block Designs I. The Method of Paired Comparisons," *Biometrika,* Vol. 39, 1952, pp. 324–345.

[4] Gridgeman, N. T., "Statistics and Taste Testing," *Applied Statistics,* Vol. 9, 1960, pp. 103–112.

[5] Howorth, W. S. and Oliver, P. H., "The Application of Multiple Factor Analysis to the Assessment of Fabric Handle," *Journal of the Textile Institute,* Vol. 49, 1959, pp. T540–T553.

[6] Glenn, W. A. and David, H. A., "Ties in Paired-Comparison Experiments Using a Modified Thurstone-Mosteller Model," *Biometrics,* Vol. 16, 1960, pp. 86–109.

[7] Bradley, R. A., "Rank Analysis of Incomplete Block Designs II. Additional Tables for the Method of Paired Comparisons," *Biometrika,* Vol. 41, 1954, pp. 502–537.

[8] Dykstra, O., "A Note on the Rank Analysis of Incomplete Block Designs— Applications Beyond the Scope of Existing Tables," *Biometrics,* Vol. 12, 1956, pp. 301–306.

[9] Bradley, R. A., "Rank Analysis of Incomplete Block Designs III. Some Large-

Sample Results on Estimation and Power for a Method of Paired Comparisons," *Biometrika*, Vol. 42, 1955, pp. 450–470.

[10] Bradley, R. A., "Incomplete Block Rank Analysis: On the Appropriateness of the Model for a Method of Paired Comparisons," *Biometrics*, Vol. 10, 1954, pp. 375–390.

[11] Luce, R. D., *Individual Choice Behavior*, Wiley, New York, 1959.

[12] Ford, L. R., Jr., "Solution of a Ranking Problem from Binary Comparisons," *American Mathematical Monthly*, Vol. 64, 1957, pp. 28–33.

[13] Dykstra, O., Jr., "Rank Analysis of Incomplete Block Designs: A Method of Paired Comparisons Employing Unequal Repetitions on Pairs," *Biometrics*, Vol. 16, 1960, pp. 176–188.

[14] Bose, R. C., "Paired Comparison Designs for Testing, Concordance Between Judges," *Biometrika*, Vol. 43, 1956, pp. 113–121.

[15] David, H. A., "The Structure of Cyclic Paired Comparison Designs," *Journal Australian Mathematical Society*, Vol. 3, 1963, pp. 117–127.

[16] Kendall, M. G., "Further Contributions to the Theory of Paired Comparisons," *Biometrics*, Vol. 11, 1955, pp. 43–62.

[17] Wilkinson, J. W., "An Analysis of Paired Comparison Designs with Incomplete Repetitions," *Biometrika*, Vol. 44, 1957, pp. 97–113.

[18] Thurstone, L. L., "A Law of Comparative Judgment," *Psychological Review*, Vol. 34, 1927, pp. 273–286.

[19] Jackson, J. E. and Fleckenstein, M., "An Evaluation of Some Statistical Techniques Used in the Analysis of Paired Comparison Data," *Biometrics*, Vol. 13, 1957, pp. 51–64.

[20] Mosteller, F., "Remarks on the Method of Paired Comparisons: I. The Least Squares Solution Assuming Equal Standard Deviations and Equal Correlations," *Psychometrika*, Vol. 16, 1951 a, pp. 3–9.

[21] Mosteller, F., "Remarks on the Method of Paired Comparisons: I. The Effect of an Aberrant Standard Deviation when Equal Standard Deviations and Equal Correlations are Assumed. III. A Test of Significance for Paired Comparisons when Equal Standard Deviations and Equal Correlations are Assumed," *Psychometrika*, Vol. 16, 1951 b, pp. 203–218.

[22] Morrissey, J. H., "New Method for the Assignment of Psychometric Scale Values from Incomplete Paired Comparisons," *Journal of the Optical Society of America*, Vol. 45, 1955, pp. 373–378.

[23] Gulliksen, H., "A Least Squares Solution for Paired Comparisons with Incomplete Data," *Psychometrika*, Vol. 21, 1956, pp. 125–134.

[24] Gridgeman, N. T., "Application of a Quantal-Response Theory to the Cross Comparison of Taste-Stimule Intensities," *Biometrics*, Vol. 14, 1958, p. 548.

[25] Maxwell, A. E., "Maximum Likelihood Estimates of Item Parameters Using the Logistic Function," *Psychometrika*, Vol. 24, 1959, p. 221.

[26] Bradley, R. A., Katti, S. K., and Coons, I. J., "Optimal Scaling for Ordered Categories," Office of Naval Research, 1961, ASTIA Catalogue No. 265152.

[27] Bliss, C. I., Greenwood, M. L., and White, E. S., "A Rankit Analysis of Paired Comparisons for Measuring the Effect of Sprays on Flavor," *Biometrics*, Vol. 12, 1956, pp. 381–403.

[28] Fisher, R. A. and Yates, F., *Statistical Tables for Biological, Agricultural and Medical Research*, 4th ed., Oliver and Boyd, London, 1953.

[29] Wei, T. H., "The Algebraic Foundations of Ranking Theory," unpublished thesis, Cambridge University, England, 1952.

[30] Doehlert, D. H., "Estimating Rank Order by Triad Reduction," thesis, 1962, University of Delaware.

[31] Scheffe, H., "An Analysis of Variance for Paired Comparisons," *Journal of the American Statistical Association*, Vol. 47, 1952, pp. 273–286.

[32] Fleckenstein, M., Freund, R. A., and Jackson, J. E., "A Paired Comparison Test of Typewriter Carbon Papers," *Tappi*, Vol. 41, 1958, pp. 128–130.

[33] Cochran, W. G. and Cox, G. M., *Experimental Designs*, 2nd ed., Wiley, New York, 1957.

[*34*] Kitagawa, T. and Mitome, M., *Tables for the Design of Factorial Experiments*, Dover, New York, 1957.
[*35*] Durbin, J., "Incomplete Blocks in Ranking Experiments," *British Journal of Psychology* (Statistical Section), Vol. 4, 1951, pp. 85–90.
[*36*] Calvin, L. D., "Doubly Balanced Incomplete Block Designs for Experiments in which the Treatment Effects are Correlated," *Biometrics,* Vol. 10, 1954, pp. 61–88.
[*37*] Pendergrass, R. N. and Bradley, R. A., "Ranking in Triple Comparisons," *Contributions to Probability and Statistics,* Olkin, I. et al, eds., Stanford University Press, Stanford, Calif., 1960.
[*38*] Park, G. T., "Sensory Testing by Triple Comparisons," *Biometrics,* Vol. 17, 1961, pp. 251–260.

Amos Turk[1]

Concentrations of Odorous Vapors in Test Chambers

REFERENCE: Turk, Amos, **"Concentrations of Odorous Vapors in Test Chambers,"** *Basic Principles of Sensory Evaluation, ASTM STP 433,* American Society for Testing and Materials, 1968, pp. 79–83.

Odor test chambers are used either for evaluation of odor-reducing devices, or to provide odor-free environments in which a jury can measure the odors of materials, products, or foods. It is important to consider the factors that determine the changing and equilibrium concentrations of odorous vapors in such chambers.

Processes that tend to increase the concentration of odorous vapors are:

(*a*) generation of vapor within (or injection into) the space, and

(*b*) introduction of vapor by replacement of chamber air by ventilation or infiltration with outdoor air of higher vapor concentration.

Processes that tend to decrease the concentration of odorous vapor are:

(*a*) treatment of the chamber air by a vapor-reducing device (for example, activated carbon recirculator), and

(*b*) removal of vapor by replacement of chamber air by ventilation or infiltration with outdoor air of lower vapor concentration.

The concentration of odorous vapor in a chamber will approach an equilibrium value in which the rates of vapor-reducing and vapor-increasing processes are equal. If it is assumed that air introduced into the chamber by ventilation, infiltration, or recirculation through a treatment device is completely and instantaneously mixed with the chamber air, then the concentration of vapors at any time and at equilibrium are given by the following equations:[2]

[1] Professor, Department of Chemistry, The City College of the City University of New York, New York, Personal member ASTM.

[2] Turk, A., "Measurements of Odorous Vapors in Test Chambers: Theoretical," *ASHRAE Journal,* Oct. 1963, p. 55.

$$C = C_0 e^{-(Q_i + EQ_r)t/V} + \frac{C_i Q_i + G}{Q_i + EQ_r}[1 - e^{-(Q_i + EQ_r)t/V}]$$

$$C_\infty = \frac{C_i Q_i + G}{Q_i + EQ_r}$$

where:

V = volume of chamber,
t = time,
C = concentration of vapor in chamber at any time,
C_0 = initial concentration of vapor in chamber,
C_∞ = concentration of vapor in chamber at equilibrium,
C_i = concentration of vapor in ventilation or infiltration air,
C_r = concentration of vapor delivered by the air treatment device,
E = efficiency of vapor reduction by the air treatment device,
Q_i = volume rate of ventilation or infiltration,
Q_r = volume rate of air delivered by the air treatment device, and
G = quantity rate of generation of vapor within (or injected into) chamber.

Simplified equations apply to the following special cases:

(a) Ventilation air is pure ($C_i = 0$).

$$C = C_0 e^{-(Q_i + EQ_r)t/V} + \frac{G}{(Q_i + EQ_r)}[1 - e^{-(Q_i + EQ_r)t/V}]$$

$$C_\infty = \frac{G}{(Q_i + EQ_r)}$$

(b) No vapor is being generated or injected ($G = 0$).

$$C = C_0 e^{-(Q_i + EQ_r)t/V} + \frac{C_i Q_i}{(Q_i + EQ_r)}[1 - e^{-(Q_i + EQ_r)t/V}]$$

and

$$C_\infty = \frac{C_i Q_i}{(Q_i + EQ_r)}$$

(c) The vapor reducing device is 100 per cent efficient ($E = 1$ and $C_r = 0$).

$$C = C_0 e^{-(Q_i + Q_r)t/V} + \frac{C_i Q_i + G}{Q_i + Q_r}[1 - e^{-(Q_i + Q_r)t/V}]$$

and

$$C_\infty = \frac{C_i Q_i + G}{(Q_i + Q_r)}$$

(d) The chamber is originally pure ($C_0 = 0$).

$$C = \frac{C_i Q_i + G}{Q_i + EQ_r} [1 - e^{-(Q_i + EQ_r)t/V}]$$

Note that the concentration *rises* to the equilibrium value of the general case.

(e) The room is tight ($Q_i = 0$).

$$C = C_0 e^{-EQ_r t/V} + \frac{G}{EQ_r} (1 - e^{-EQ_r t/V}),$$

and

$$C_\infty = G/EQ_r .$$

(f) Combination of (o) and (b) (C_i and $G = 0$).

$$C = C_0 e^{-(Q_i + EQ_r)t/V}$$

and

$$C_\infty = 0.$$

(g) Combination of (a) and (c) ($C_i = 0$, $E = 1$, and $C_r = 0$).

$$C = C_0 e^{-(Q_i + Q_r)t/V} + \frac{G}{(Q_i + Q_r)} [1 - e^{-(Q_i + Q_r)t/V}]$$

and

$$C_\infty = \frac{G}{Q_i + Q_r} .$$

(h) Combination of (b) and (e) ($G = 0$, $Q_i = 0$).

$$C = C_0 e^{-EQ_r t/V}$$

and

$$C_\infty = 0.$$

(i) Combination of (a), (b), and (c) ($C_i = 0$, $G = 0$, $E = 1$, and $C_r = 0$).

$$C = C_0 e^{-(Q_i + Q_r)t/V}$$

and

$$C_\infty = 0.$$

Expression in Terms of Air Changes

An air change is the addition to the chamber of a volume of air equal to the volume of the chamber. Then the number (N) of air changes (dimensionless) per unit time is given by:

$$N/t = Q/V$$

or

$$N = Qt/V.$$

Mixing Factor

In any expression of the general form $e^{-Qt/V}$ or e^{-N}, a mixing factor, m, may be applied to account for the fact that dilution of air is not instantaneous, and that concentration fall-off rates are actually smaller than the ideal values given by the equations developed here. It has been suggested[3] that m commonly ranges between one third and one tenth.

Sensory Testing

The efficiency of a vapor-reducing device may be measured by sensory methods that obviate the need for determination of material concentrations. If we select a sealed chamber in which no odor is being generated (Case h), then the ratio of concentrations C_1/C_2 corresponding to any two times t_1 and t_2 during the operation of the device is

$$C_1/C_2 = e^{(EQ_r m/V)(t_2 - t_1)}$$

It is possible to measure the ratio of two suprathreshold concentrations of odorous vapor C_1/C_2 by either a dilution or a matching technique (for example, ASTM Method for Measurement of Odor in Atmospheres (Dilution Method), (D 1391 – 57)).

Let

$$P = \frac{\text{volume of air sample diluted to threshold}}{\text{volume of original air sample}} = C/C_t.$$

Then, the ratio of P values for any two concentrations C_1/C_2 is:

$$P_1/P_2 = C_1/C_2$$

The relationship expressed logarithmically is:

$$\log_{10} P_1/P_2 = 0.434 \ (EQ_r m/V)(t_2 - t_1)$$

The latter equation may be used to calculate the efficiency of a vapor reducing device in the chamber from odor dilution methods determined at different times, or to calculate the time interval between sensory tests that is needed to provide a specified diminution of vapor concentration.

Example 1—In a 1000-ft³ sealed room, 50 ft³/min of air is recirculated by an air purifier. The mixing factor is estimated to be one third. The P value, measured by a dilution method, is found to be 50. Two hours and 40 min later the value has dropped to 10. What is the efficiency of the unit?

[3] Bried, R. S., "Simple Way to Determine Air Contaminants," *Air Engineering*, Vol. 2, 1960, p. 39.

Answer:

Solving the last equation for E, we have,

$$E = \frac{2.303 \log_{10} P_1/P_2}{(Q_r m/V)(t_2 - t_1)}$$

$$E = \frac{2.303 \log_{10} (50/10)}{\dfrac{50(\frac{1}{3})}{1000} \times 160}$$

$$E = 0.60 \quad \text{or} \quad 60 \text{ per cent}$$

Example 2—The room of Example 1 used as a chamber for conducting sensory odor tests. After a test is concluded, the purifying unit is turned on to clear the air in preparation for a subsequent test. If the vapor concentration is to be reduced by 90 per cent, how much time must elapse between tests?

Answer:

$$C_2 = C_1 - 0.9\, C_1 = 0.1\, C_1$$

$$t_2 - t_1 = \frac{2.303 \log_{10} C_1/C_2}{E Q_r m/V}$$

$$t_2 - t_1 = \frac{2.303 \log_{10} 10}{\dfrac{0.60\ (50)(\frac{1}{3})}{1000}}$$

$$t_2 - t_1 = 230 \text{ min, or 3 h 50 min}$$

B. P. McNamara[1]

Measurement of Irritation

REFERENCE: McNamara, B. P., **"Measurement of Irritation,"** *Basic Principles of Sensory Evaluation, ASTM STP 433,* American Society for Testing and Materials, 1968, pp. 84–97.

Physiological Background

General

Irritation is a local action on the skin or mucosal tissue. It can be induced by thermal, mechanical, chemical, or electrical stimulation. The stimulation evokes impulses from the receptor organ. The impulses may be conveyed over neural pathways to the brain where they are translated into perceptual sensations, that is, warmth, cold, itching, pain. Impulses also may be carried to muscles or glands which react to the stimulus.

The pathway from the receptor to the effector is known as the reflex arc (see Fig. 1). It consists of an afferent nerve (sensory) carrying impulses to the spinal cord and an efferent nerve (motor) carrying impulses from the central nervous system (spinal cord and brain) to the effector muscles or glands. In some reflexes only the afferent and the efferent nerves are involved. In most reflexes one or more connector (internuncial, intercalated) nerves may be interposed between the afferent and the efferent nerve. These connector nerves may transport the impulse to higher levels of the spinal cord and brain or to lower levels of the spinal cord and thereby produce perceptual responses or effector organ reactions in many areas of the body [1].[2]

Some responses to irritation have been attributed to axon reflexes [2]. This reflex does not necessarily involve the spinal cord or central nervous system. An impulse passing centrally on an afferent nerve may spread and travel peripherally on a branch of that nerve (dotted line on Fig. 1).

[1] Chief, Toxicology Dept., Medical Research Laboratory, Research Laboratories, Edgewood Arsenal, Md.

[2] The italic numbers in brackets refer to the list of references appended to this paper.

Receptors

The peripheral termination of afferent nerves are bare fibers or other specialized endings. These receptors respond most effectively to specific types of stimuli. Receptors are located in the skin (see Fig. 2), muscles, tendons, respiratory tract, digestive tract, mesentery, carotid sinus, and other internal organs. They are also contained in special sense organs as those of sight, smell, taste, and hearing.

Receptors for irritation include the specialized nerve endings in the

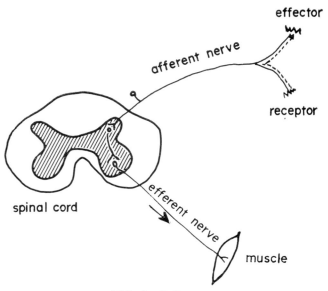

FIG. 1—*Reflex arc.*

skin and the bare nerve endings in the muscles and mucosal tissue. Irritation of the olfactory end organs in the nose may be partially involved in sneezing [3].

Afferent Nerves

Nerve fibers from the skin and muscles are gathered into a compound unit which enters the dorsal routes of the spinal cord [4], or through certain of the cranial nerves [5,6].

Nerve fibers in a sensory (afferent) nerve are predominately of two groups, A and C, based on diameter of the fiber and conduction velocity of the nerve impulse. The nerve impulse travels faster in the larger fibers. C fibers in mammals are about 1 μm in diameter and conduct at the rate of 0.5 to 2.0 m/s.

The A fibers consist of four-size groups (alpha, beta, gamma, delta) whose diameters vary from 20 to 1 μm, and velocities from 100 to 5 m/s. The A fibers are surrounded by a thick myelin sheath. The C fibers [7,8] are unmyelinated.

Pain reflexes and presumably pain are conducted by C fibers [7]. These fibers also conduct impulses associated with itching [9]. The relief of itching by rubbing may be an inhibitory interaction between fast A

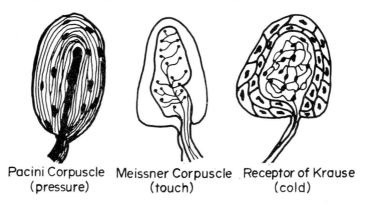

Pacini Corpuscle   Meissner Corpuscle   Receptor of Krause
(pressure)   (touch)   (cold)

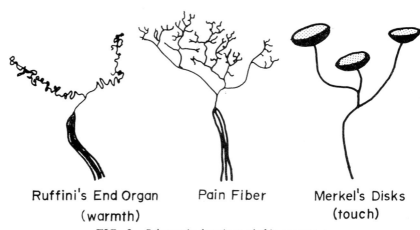

Ruffini's End Organ   Pain Fiber   Merkel's Disks
(warmth)   (touch)

FIG. 2—*Schematic drawings of skin receptors.*

fibers and slower C fibers. Pain impulses are also conducted in the A-delta fibers.

Sensory Paths of the Spinal Cord

Most sensory fibers ascend the spinal cord in the posterior column or the spinothalamic tracts. Pressure and touch impulses travel in both pathways. Sensations of pain, warmth, cold, tickle, itch, and feelings of muscular fatigue pass through the spinothalamic tract exclusively. The posterior columns are especially concerned with those impulses which control fine discriminations of intensities of pressure or size and texture of objects which contact the skin [10,11].

Sensory Paths of the Brain

At the upper border of the medulla oblongata impulses of cranial nerves are added to the ascending sensory systems [12]. These nerves and associated sensory function are as follows:
1. Olfactory nerve—smell
2. Optic—vision
5. Trigeminal—pain, temperature, touch-pressure in face, mouth, and few other areas
7. Facial—taste in anterior ⅔ of tongue; sensation to soft palate
8. Acoustic—hearing, equilibrium
9. Glossopharyngeal—taste in posterior ⅓ tongue; sensation to fauces, tonsils, pharynx, and soft palate
10. Vagus—sensory fibers from heart, lungs, bronchi, trachea, larynx, pharynx, gastrointestinal tract, external ear

The spinothalamic tracts and the posterior route end in the ventrolateral nucleus of the thalamus. Sensory fibers of the 5th, 7th, and 10th cranial nerves course to the arcuate nucleus of the thalamus. Connections from both thalamic nuclei project to the postcentral gyrus of the cortex [11].

Central Effector Mechanisms

Impulses from the sensory cortex of the brain are then transferred to motor cortex and thence over the pyramidal and extrapyramidal systems to the efferent neurones to the effector muscles or glands [13].

Efferent Nerves

The efferent nerves leave the central nervous system through the ventral roots of the spinal cord or through certain of the 3rd, 4th, 6th, 7th, 9th, 10th, 11th, or 12th cranial nerves.

Effector Organs and Their Responses to Irritation

1. Skin—The skin possesses distinctive sense organs. These are: Meissner's corpuscles for touch, Krause's end bulb for cold, Ruffini's nerve-endings for warmth, Pacinian corpuscles for deep pressure, Merkel's disks for touch, and bare nerve endings for pain. Tickling and itching appear to be due to the summed effects of stimulating both touch and pain endings. Itching which occurs spontaneously and in the absence of external stimuli may result from mild stimulation of pain fibers alone [14].

The first response to irritation is an increase in circulation of the irritated area. This is brought about as the result of an axon reflex. The vasodilatation may be accompanied by a feeling of warmth and sometimes itching or pain [2]. Hyperalgesia or hyperesthesia may develop and normally innocuous contacts, such as the rubbing of clothing, may result in unpleasant sensations and pain [15]. Hyperalgesia may extend to adjacent areas well beyond the site of primary irritation. Moreover, irritation may influence functions in areas remote from the primary site. Irritant drugs have been applied to the skin to relieve pain arising from intestinal spasm [2,16].

Prolonged irritation of the skin causes increase in dilatation and permeability of the capillaries [2]. Plasma escapes into the extracellular spaces, fluid collects under the epidermis, and blisters may form. Desquamation may follow prolonged irritation.

Irritation which may be slightly damaging on acute exposures may be severely damaging to the skin on repeated exposures [17].

Contact with certain substances produces a phenomenon known as sensitization. The sensitizer may produce no noticeable effect on the initial contact. After several exposures dermatitis may be produced by a single application of the causative agent at the area of contact or in other parts of the body.

2. *Eyes*—The cornea contains bare nerve endings which mediate pain. Cold, warm, and touch endings are lacking. There is a general belief that local stimulus results only in pain. The sensation of cold can be elicited from the cornea, and some report that sensation of touch without pain can be caused by mild stimulation of a jet of saline solution [18].

While pain is the outstanding sensation resulting from eye irritation, a number of objective effects are produced. Lacrimation, blinking, and blepharospasm are induced reflexively by stimulation of the nerve endings of the cornea or conjunctiva (ophthalmic division of the 5th nerve) [19]. Redness and swelling may develop in the conjunctiva and the iris. Scarring and opacity may develop in the cornea [20]. Damage in the iris or cornea may seriously impair vision.

3. *Respiratory system*—The respiratory tract is made up of conducting airways of the nose, pharynx, trachea, and bronchi. These airways become successively smaller and generously branched. The smallest airways end in small sacs known as alveoli. The exchange of oxygen, carbon dioxide, and other gaseous metabolites between the atmosphere and the blood is accomplished in the alveoli. The tissues of the conducting airways and those of the alveoli are very different. The airways have muscular tissue which can constrict and cause respiratory distress and asthmatic responses. This area of the lungs is lined with tough layers of cells which bear whip-like fibers called cilia. The cilia sweep inhaled foreign sub-

stances upward and out of the lungs. The bronchial lining contains glands which secrete mucus. The deep lungs where gases are exchanged do not have the protective layer [21].

Irritation of the mucous membranes of the nose elicits sneezing. Irritation beyond the nose causes coughing. Impulses for a sneeze originate in the sensory receptors of the trigeminal nerves and perhaps the olfactory end organs. Those for cough arise in the pharyngeal distribution of the glossopharyngeal nerve and the sensory endings of the vagus in the larynx, trachea, and bronchi. Both reflexes cause deep inspiration and violent expiration. The vocal cords close during inspiration when coughing. Irritation of the larynx may cause spasm of the glottis, and irritation of the deeper passages may result in bronchoconstriction [22–24].

In addition to sneeze and cough a reflex-produced apnea sometimes follows inhalation of irritant chemicals [23]. Chemical irritation of the respiratory system may be accompanied by a feeling of discomfort, pain, and suffocation. Copious secretions may occur during and for several minutes after exposure. The ciliary action may be affected also.

Discharge of mechanoreceptors by introduction of foreign bodies of abrupt pressure changes in the tracheobronchial system inhibits phrenic motoneuron discharge and causes expiratory effort and bronchoconstriction. The most sensitive zone for mechanical stimulation is the inner surface of the larynx. The tracheal bifurcation and the lower half of the trachea are sensitive, but the main bronchi are relatively insensitive [25].

When irritants pass beyond the bronchi and enter the alveoli other signs develop. All permeability is effected, and fluid from the blood stream may enter the alveolar spaces [21]. This impairs the exchange of gases and could possibly result in death.

With mild exposures the consequences of irritation may not be observable. However, persons with existing lung or heart damage may be less tolerant than healthy persons to mild lung irritation. Repeated or continued irritation, even to mild exposures, may lead to definite organic damage. The sequelae might be bronchitis, fibrotic changes, emphysema, lowered resistance to infection, and perhaps increased susceptibility to lung cancer [21].

4. *Gastrointestinal tract*—The general effects of irritation of the gastrointestinal tract are similar to those for irritation of the skin. Mild irritation of the gastrointestinal tract produces a feeling of warmth and comfort. Such action is caused by some condiments and carminative drugs [26]. Intense irritation of the gastrointestinal tract produced by ingested cantharidin produces vomiting, purging, abdominal pain, and shock [27]. Mechanical distention of the esophagus produces a gradual transition from substernal fullness to pain-like sensations [28].

5. *Genitourinary tract*—A few irritant drugs, especially cantharides,

are excreted by the kidneys and irritate the urinary tract. Irritation of the bladder causes urgency of urination and irritation of the urethra sometimes results in priapism [27].

Test Methods for Irritants

The responses of the various parts of the body to irritation have been observed, recorded, and frequently quantitated. On the basis of such information the U.S. Food and Drug Administration has standardized tests for irritation of the skin and mucous membranes. Many of the techniques used to study irritation could be adapted as testing procedures for specialized phases in the relatively broad field of irritation.

Recognized Tests

Draize has described the tests for irritants used by the U.S. Food and Drug Administration [17,29]. A primary irritation of the skin is measured by single and repeated direct applications on clipped rabbits. Erythema and edema are scored at 24 and 72 h after exposure. More severe damage such as later necrosis and eschar formation are also noted.

Primary irritation of mucous membranes should be evaluated on the membrane of specific interest. However, Draize describes the use of vaginal and penile mucosa in dogs and the eye mucosa in rabbits.

Methods to test for sensitization, a phenomenon in which repeated exposures may provoke reactions at the site of application or in tissues remote from the area of application, are also described. Sensitization studies in man and guinea pig are mentioned.

"Use" tests in which a substance is tested on a panel of persons is also included. Several of these tests are also described in "Hazardous Substances, Regulations under the Federal Hazardous Substances Labeling Act, Part 191, Chapter 1, Title 21, Code of the Federal Regulations, U.S. Department of Health, Education, and Welfare, Food and Drug Administration, Federal Registers, 12 Aug. 1961" [30].

Circulation in the Skin

Reviews on cutaneous circulation have been written by Furchgott [31], Paton [32], Herxheimer [33], Methods in Medical Research [34,35], Hensel and Bender [36], Barany [37], Fox and Wyatt [39].

Toh et al [40] have reported on the effects of capsaicin, vanillylamine, and other chemical irritants on the blood flow in perfused rabbit ears. Crimson et al [41] have studied blood flow in the forearm. Doerr and Heite [42] describe calorimetric and photometric techniques for measurement of skin blood flow. A photographic method for study of circulation in the cheek pouch of hamsters has been described by Fulton et al [43].

Vascular permeability may be studied by a number of methods. A widely used method in animals depends on leakage of protein-bound dye from the plasma into the skin. Usually the dye is injected intravenously and the test substance intradermally. The size and intensity of color in the skin reflect the degree of capillary leakage [33]. Miles and Miles [44] used a dye technique to investigate factors which influence reactivity of the skin. They noted differences in skin response of the ear, back, flank, and abdomen of guinea pigs. Demis et al [45], Stewart and Bliss [46], and Herxheimer and Schachter [47] have utilized Evans blue dye in man.

A number of investigators have reported upon measurement of inflammatory edema in man and animals [48–53].

Pain

Since pain and irritation are related phenomena the vast literature on the former may serve a useful purpose in study of the latter. The extensive reviews by Beecher [16,28] thoroughly cover pain of all body areas. These reviews discuss the pain apparatus, pain stimuli, methods of measuring pain in animals and man, the pain threshold, factors causing variation in pain threshold, and other factors concerning pain.

More recent reviews on the physiology of pain [54–58] are also recommended.

Irritation in the Eyes

The U.S. Food and Drug Administration's test for irritation of rabbit eyes has been previously described. Doyle et al [59] employed an eye irritation panel for the study of air pollutants. Similar research has been reported by Schuch and Renzetti [60] and Wayne and Orcutt [61].

Respiratory System

The effects of airborne irritating substances have been a major concern in the fields of air pollution and public health. Quantitative measurements of changes in lung function induced by irritants have been made in animals and in man. Additional *in vivo* and *in vitro* reactions to irritation possibly could serve to measure or to reflect irritant action in the respiratory system.

1. *Physiological responses in man*—Widely accepted clinical tests for lung function have been described by Comroe et al [62] and by DuBois [63]. These tests measure the tidal volume; inspiratory reserve volume; expiratory reserve volume; residual volume; total lung capacity; vital capacity; inspiratory capacity; functional residual capacity; respiratory rate; respiratory dead space; alveolar ventilation; ventilation/blood flow ratios in the lung; diffusion of oxygen from the alveoli to the capillaries; arterial oxygen, carbon dioxide, and pH; the mechanical factors of breathing; elastic properties of the lungs or thorax; and airway resistance. It is expected that acute or chronic exposures to inhaled irritants would

alter some of the aforementioned measurements [64]. Motley and Kuz-man [65] showed significant differences in arterial oxygen saturation, pulmonary compliance, and the degree of emphysema before and after smoking. Branscomb [66] states that flow measurements taken near the end of expiration reveal early lung disease not apparent with other measurements.

A simple apparatus to detect diffuse bronchial obstruction was de-scribed by Jarvinen [67].

Impairment of pharyngeal reflexes in man has been attributed to me-chanical and chemical action of dust containing silicates [68].

Dautreband [69] described a volumetric pneumograph for quantitative study of constricting and dilating aerosols on whole lung.

2. *Responses in animals*—Amdur [70–72] examined the effects of gases on airway resistance in guinea pigs.

Pulmonary vasoconstriction, airway changes, increased pulmonary artery pressure, decreased cardiac activity, and shock resulting from in-halation of sulfur dioxide in anesthetized dogs were demonstrated by Salem and Aviado [73].

The demonstrations of reflexes resulting from irritation of the upper respiratory tract are discussed by Dautreband [74]. Responses of excised guinea pig lungs during exposure to irritants [75] are also mentioned by Dautreband.

Long [76] used the respiratory uptake of $CO_2(C^{14})$ and oxygen as a measure of pulmonary irritation in rats.

Histological Studies

Histochemical studies after sudden, noncancerous deaths revealed presence of tarry residues (from smoke and other air pollutants) in lungs, lymphatics, liver, and spleen [77].

The tendency of dusts to cause fibrosis in lungs of rats was determined at one, two, and four months [78].

Fibrogenic properties of silica and other dusts have been studied on the subcutaneous connective tissue of a pneumodermal pouch of rats. The pouch was formed by injection of air and diluted croton oil under the skin [79].

Recent advances in use of roentgenograms suggest that direct visualiza-tion of the intact lung may become a useful method for detecting changes produced by foreign substances [80].

Pace [81–83] studied the effect of air pollutant material on multiplica-tion, growth, and respiration of cultures of cells of mouse fibroblasts, mouse liver cells, mouse and human skin cells, and human bronchial and alveolar epithelial cells.

Biochemical and Immunological Studies

The deposition of silicates in the lung induces biochemical and immunological changes. Finulli and Chislandi [84] noted an increase in serum neuraminic acid in silicotic patients. It has been reported that the stage of evolution of the disease is related to the amount of serum glycoproteins [85].

Gast [86,87] also studied the effect of air pollutants upon enzyme systems of the blood, intestinal muscle, and bacteria. Mountain and Scheel [88] studied changes in enzyme systems of the lungs as a result of action by irritant air pollutants. It has been hypothesized that silica dust modifies the microphage cells which have phagocytized it to form antigenic substances [89–91].

Gastrointestinal Tract

Irritation influences the muscular movements of the gastrointestinal tract [92]. These movements can be measured and recorded from normal animals and man by use of swallowed balloons. Small transducers to record pressure changes have been used in place of the balloon [93, 94].

Measurement of movements of the gastrointestinal tract has long been a normal part of the curriculum in the teaching of physiology and pharmacology. A number of techniques are described by Jackson [95].

Daphnia magna is a fresh water crustacean about 0.1 in. in length. It is sufficiently transparent to permit visualization of its gastrointestinal tract. Chemical irritants placed in the liquid medium surrounding the organism can be easily studied.

The gastrointestinal activity in the frog [96], the pigeon [97], and the dog [98–101] has been frequently studied. The contractions of isolated musculature from various animals has been widely employed in biological research [102].

Peritoneum

A "writhing syndrome" can be produced in mice following the intraperitoneal injection of numerous drugs and chemicals. The animals exhibit intermittent contractions of the abdomen, twisting and turning of the trunk, and extension of the hind legs. This is believed to represent a reaction to an irritating or painful stimulus [103].

Bare nerve endings mediating pain are present in serous surfaces of the peritoneum [18]. Touch, cold, and warm endings are absent.

Psychological

Some responses to irritation are automatic while others are influenced by a perceptual component. Stimulation of the sensory receptors evokes impulses which pass over afferent nerves and internuncial nerves and reach the brain where they are transformed to sensations or perceptions. The sensation produced and the reaction thereto differs in different individuals, and may differ in the same individual at different times and under different circumstances. The sensation and subsequent reaction is influenced by the previous experience of the subject and also by other stimuli and sensations which may be simultaneously augmenting or diminishing that produced by the irritant. Thus, under different conditions or in different persons an irritation of the skin may evoke (*a*) no sensation, (*b*) itching, or (*c*) pain.

Dizziness and poor concentration, reduction or loss of corneal, and conjunctival and pharyngeal reflexes noted during silicosis were attributed to central and not peripheral origin [*104*].

Psychological testing, wherein a condition is imposed upon the normal or experimentally controlled behavior in man or animal, has been employed extensively in the last decade [*105,106*]. These tests are concerned with activity, learning, emotion, discrimination, motivation, etc. Although applicable this methodology has been used sparingly in the study of irritants. It has been reported by Boche [*107*] that volitional running activity of rats is reduced by exposure to atmospheres containing dilute air pollutants.

References

[1] Best, C. H. and Taylor, N. B., *Physiological Basis of Medical Practice,* ed. VI, Williams & Wilkins, 1955, p. 933.
[2] Goodman and Gilman, *Pharmacological Basis of Therapeutics,* 2nd ed., Macmillan Co., 1956, p. 1021.
[*3*] Bard, Philip, *Medical Physiology,* 10th ed., Mosby, 1956, p. 380.
[*4*] Fulton, *Textbook of Physiology,* 17th ed., Saunders, 1955, p. 54.
[*5*] Fulton, *Textbook of Physiology,* 17th ed., Saunders, 1955, p. 341.
[*6*] Netter, F., "Nervous System," *Ciba Collection of Medical Illustrations,* Vol. 1, 1958, p. 42.
[*7*] Fulton, *Textbook of Physiology,* 17th ed., Saunders, 1955, p. 334.
[*8*] Bard, Philip, *Medical Physiology,* 10th ed., 1956, Mosby, 1956, p. 937.
[*9*] Fulton, *Textbook of Physiology,* 17th ed., Saunders, 1955, p. 361.
[*10*] Fulton, *Textbook of Physiology,* 17th ed., Saunders, 1955, pp. 336–340.
[*11*] Neter, F., "Nervous System," *Ciba Collection of Medical Illustrations,* plates 33, 34, Vol. 1, 1958, pp. 58–59.
[*12*] Netter, F., "Nervous System," *Ciba Collection of Medical Illustration,* plate 20, Vol. 1, 1958, p. 42.
[*13*] Netter, F., "Nervous System," *Ciba Collection of Medical Illustrations,* plates 43, 44, Vol. 1, 1958, pp. 68–69.
[*14*] Best, C. H. and Taylor, N. B., *Physiological Basis of Medical Practice,* ed. VI, Williams & Wilkins, 1955, p. 933.
[*15*] Fulton, *Textbook of Physiology,* 17th ed., Saunders, 1955, p. 358.
[*19*] Beecher, H. K., *Pharmacological Reviews,* Vol. 9, 1957, p. 143.
[*17*] Draize, J. H., *Food, Drug, and Cosmetic Law,* Vol. 132, 1955, p. 731.
[*18*] Best, C. H. and Taylor, N. B., *Physiological Basis of Medical Practice,* ed. VI, Williams & Wilkins, 1955, p. 938.
[*19*] Best, C. H. and Taylor, N. B., *Physiological Basis of Medical Practice,* ed. VI Williams & Wilkins, 1955, p. 1107.

[20] Draize, J. H., *Food, Drug, and Cosmetic Law,* Vol. 132, 1955, p. 724.
[21] Nelson, N., *Proceedings National Conference on Air Pollution,* U.S. Department of Health, Education, and Welfare, Nov. 1958, p. 210.
[22] Best, C. H. and Taylor, N. B., *Physiological Basis of Medical Practice,* ed. VI, Williams & Wilkins, 1955, p. 354.
[23] Bard, Philip, *Medical Physiology,* 10th ed., Mosby, 1956, p. 380.
[24] Fulton, *Textbook of Physiology,* 17th ed., Saunders, 1955, p. 389.
[25] Fulton, *Textbook of Physiology,* 17th ed., Saunders, 1955, p. 389.
[26] *Remington's Practice of Pharmacy,* 12th ed., Mack Publishing, 1961, p. 598.
[27] Goodman and Gilman, *Pharmacological Basis of Therapeutics,* ed. II, Macmillan, 1956, p. 1022.
[28] Beecher, H. K., *Measurement of Subjective Responses,* Oxford University Press, New York, 1959, p. 38.
[29] Draize, J. H., *Supply of Chemicals in Food, Drugs, and Cosmetics,* Association of Food and Drug Officials of the U.S., 1959, p. 46.
[30] *Hazardous Substances,* Regulations under the Federal Hazardous Substance Labeling Act, Part 191, Chapter 1, Title 21, Code of the Federal Regulations, US Department of Health, Education, and Welfare, Food and Drug Administration, Federal Register, 12 Aug. 1961.
[31] Furchgott, R. F., *Pharmacological Review,* Vol. 7, 1955, p. 183.
[32] Paton, W. D. M., *Progress in the Biological Sciences in Relation to Dermatology,* Cambridge University Press, 1960, p. 429.
[33] Herxheimer, A., *Annual Review of Pharmacology,* Vol. 1, 1961, p. 351.
[34] *Methods in Medical Research,* Vol. 1, 1948, p. 66.
[35] *Methods in Medical Research,* Vol. 8, 1960, p. 222.
[36] Hensel, H. and Bender, F., *Archives des Physiologiques,* Plugers, Vol. 263, 1956, p. 603.
[37] Barany, F. R., *Acta Medica Scandinavica,* Supplement, 1955, p. 304.
[38] Burch, G. E., *Circulation,* Vol. 13, 1956, p. 641.
[39] Fox, R. H. and Wyatt, H. T., *Journal of Physiology,* Vol. 151, 1960, p. 30.
[40] Toh, C. C., Lee, T. S., and Kiang, A. K., *British Journal of Pharmacology,* Vol. 10, 1955, p. 175.
[41] Crimson, et al, *Journal of Physiology,* Vol. 145, 1959, p. 47.
[42] Doerr, F. F. and Heite, H. J., *Archiv für Klinische und Expermentelle Dermatologie,* Vol. 204, 1957, p. 543.
[43] Fulton, G. P., Farber, F. M., and Moreci, A. P., *Journal of Investigative Dermatology,* Vol. 33, 1959, p. 317.
[44] Miles, A. A. and Miles, E. M., *Journal of Physiology,* Vol. 118, 1952, p. 228.
[45] Demis, D. J., M. J. Davis, and Lawler, J. C., *Journal of Investigative Dermatology,* Vol. 34, 1960, p. 43.
[46] Stewart, P. B. and Bliss, J. Q., *British Journal of Experimental Pathology,* Vol. 38, 1957, p. 462.
[47] Herxheimer, A. and Schachter, M., *Nature,* Vol. 183, 1958, p. 1510.
[48] Pfeiffer, C. C., Jenney, E. H., and Williams, H. L., *Journal of Laboratory & Clinical Medicine,* Vol. 32, 1947, p. 1386.
[49] Smith, W. and Humphrey, J. H., *British Journal of Experimental Pathology,* Vol. 30, 1949, p. 560.
[50] Humphrey, J. H., *British Journal of Experimental Pathology,* Vol. 32, 1951, p. 274.
[51] Squire, J. R., *Clinical Science,* Vol. 9, 1950, p. 127.
[52] Bain, W. A., Hellier, F. F., and Warin R. P., *Lancet,* Vol. 2, 1948, p. 964.
[53] Holti, G., *Clinical Science,* Vol. 14, 1955, p. 143.
[54] Gerard, R. W., *Annals of the New York Academy of Sciences* Vol. 86, 1960, p. 6.
[55] Lasagna, L., *Annals of the New York Academy of Sciences,* Vol. 86, 1960, p. 28.
[56] Petrie, A., *Annals of the New York Academy of Sciences,* Vol. 86, 1960, p. 13.

[57] Lim, R. K. S., *Annals of the New York Academy of Sciences,* Vol. 86, 1960, p. 83.
[58] Kutscher, A. H. and Kutscher, H. W., *Internat Record of Medicine and General Practice Clinic,* Vol. 170, 1957, p. 202.
[59] Doyle, G. J., Endow, N. and Jones S. L., *Archives of Environmental Health,* Vol. 3, 1961, p. 657.
[60] Schuch, E. A. and Renzetti, N. A., *Journal of Air Pollution Control Association,* Vol. 10, 1960, p. 389.
[61] Wayne, L. G. and Orcutt, J. A., *Journal of Occupational Medicine,* Vol. 2, 1960, p. 383.
[62] Comroe, J. H., et al, *The Lung,* Yearbook, Chicago, 1955.
[63] DuBois, A. B., "Methods for Evaluating Pulmonary Functions," CmlC Contract DA18-108-CML-6556, 1960.
[64] Motley, H. L. and Leftwich, C. I., *Journal of the American Medical Association,* Vol. 171, 1959, p. 1469.
[65] Motley, H. L. and Kurzman, W. J., *California Medicine,* Vol. 88, 1958, p. 211.
[66] Branscomb, B. V., *Public Health Reports,* Vol. 75, 1960, p. 1174.
[67] Jarvinen, K. A. J., *Annales Medicinae Internae Finniae,* Vol. 48, 1959, p. 219.
[68] Tanzariello, R. and Anastasi, N., *Clin Otorino laringoiat,* Vol. 11, 1959, p. 39.
[69] Dautreband, L., "Studies on Aerosols AEC Research Development Report," UR-530, 1958, p. 126.
[70] Amdur, M. O., *Industrial Hygene Quarterly,* June 1957, p. 149.
[71] Amdur, M. O., *American Industrial Hygiene Association Journal,* Vol. 22, 1960, p. 1.
[72] Amdur, M. O., *International Journal of Air Pollution,* Vol. 3, 1960, p. 201.
[73] Salem, H. and Aviado, D. M., *Archives of Enviromental Health,* Vol. 2, 1961, p. 56.
[74] Dautreband, L., "Studies on Aerosols AEC Research Development Report," UR-530, 1958, p. 60.
[75] Dautreband, L., "Studies on Aerosols AEC Research Development Report," UR-530, 1958, p. 170.
[76] Long, J. E., *Public Health Report,* Vol. 75, 1960, p. 1178.
[77] Mallet, L. and Heros, M., *Presse Medicale,* Vol. 33, 1959, p. 1346.
[78] Ferin, J. and Ulrich, L., *Pracovni lekarstvi (Prague),* Vol. 12, 1960, p. 344.
[79] Ottowicz, J., *Patologia polska (Warsaw),* Vol. 10, 1959, p. 325.
[80] David, A. and Soboda, M., *Pracovni lekarstvi (Prague),* Vol. 12, 1960, p. 129.
[81] Pace, D. M., *Public Health Report,* Vol. 75, 1960, p. 1184.
[82] Pace, D. M., Contract APM-121.3, U.S. Public Health Service, 1956–1958.
[83] Pace, D. M., Grant RG-6439, U. S. Public Health Service, 1958.
[84] Finulli, M. and Ghislandi, R., *Medicina del lavoro (Milan),* Vol. 50, 1959, p. 683.
[85] Buscarini,, L. and Nicrosini, F., *Medicino del lavoro (Milan)* Vol. 50, 1959, p. 368.
[86] Gast, J. H., Contract APB-13.1, U. S. Public Health Service, 1956.
[87] Gast, J. H., *Public Health Report,* Vol. 75, 1960, p. 1184.
[88] Mountain, J. T. and Scheel, L. D., Project APM-131.2, U. S. Public Health Service, 1955.
[89] Pernis, B., Gambini, G. and Finulli, M., *Medicina del lavoro (Milan),* Vol. 50, 1959, p. 250.
[90] Vigliani, E. C. and Pernis, B., *Journal of Occupational Medicine,* Vol. 1, 1959, p. 319.
[91] Gross, P., *Archives of Industrial Health,* American Medical Association, Vol. 21, 1960, p. 228.
[92] Fulton, *Textbook of Physiology,* 17th ed., 1955, Saunders, Philadelphia, pp. 1104. 1009, 1028.

[93] Brody, D. A. and Quigley, J. P., *Gastroenterology*, Vol. 9, 1947, p. 570.
[94] Quigley, J. P. and Brody, D. A., *American Journal of Medicine*, Vol. 13, 1952, p. 73.
[95] Jackson, *Experimental Pharmacology and Materia Medica*, 2d ed., Mosby, St. Louis, 1939.
[96] Jackson, *Experimental Pharmacology and Materia Medica*, 2d ed., Mosby, St. Louis, 1939, p. 380.
[97] Jackson, *Experimental Pharmacology and Materia Media*, 2d ed., Mosby, St. Louis, 1939, p. 479.
[98] Jackson, *Experimental Pharamcology and Materia Medica*, 2d ed., Mosby, St. Louis, 1939, p. 89.
[99] Jackson, *Experimental Pharmacology and Materia Media*, 2d ed., Mosby, St. Louis, 1939, p. 148.
[100] Jackson, *Experimental Pharmacology and Materia Media*, 2d ed., Mosby, St. Louis, 1939, p. 230.
[101] Jackson, *Experimental Pharmacology and Materia Media*, 2d ed., Mosby, St. Louis, 1939, p. 543.
[102] Jackson, *Experimental Pharmacology and Materia Medica*, 2d ed., Mosby, St. Louis, 1939, p. 379.
[103] *Journal of the American Medical Association Research Review*, Vol. 165, 1957, p. 427.
[104] Kuo, V. P. and Liu, Y. T., *Chinese Medical Journal (Peking)*, Vol. 78, 1959, p. 326.
[105] Hunt, H. F., *Annual Review of Pharmacology*, Vol. 1, 1961, p. 125.
[106] Uhr, L. and Miller, J. G., *Drugs and Behavior*, Wiley, New York, 1960.
[107] Boche, R. D., *Public Health Reports*, Vol. 75, 1960, p. 1185.

J. A. Hoffman[1]

Principles of Psychological Test Methods (Judgmental Methods—Appearance)

REFERENCE: Hoffman, J. A., **"Principles of Psychological Test Methods (Judgmental Methods—Appearance),** *Basic Principles of Sensory Evaluation, ASTM STP 433,* American Society for Testing and Materials, 1958, pp. 98–105.

The visual appearance of a surface or volume is related to the illumination by which it is viewed, the conditions under which it is viewed, and the visual response characteristics of the observer. The appearance characteristics of greatest interest are those relating to:
1. Luminance (brightness, lightness).
2. Specular reflectance (gloss, luster, sheen).
3. Chromaticity (hue and saturation).
4. Transparency (translucence).
5. Nonuniformity (texture, pattern, contrasting areas such as those caused by flaws or foreign substances, etc.).

Illumination

Spectral Distribution

The spectral distribution of the illumination source is of particular importance in visual judgments of luminance and chromaticity. The spectral distributions of several standard illuminants, as adopted by the Commission Internationale d'Eclairage (CIE) in 1931, are shown in Fig. 1. CIE Source A is intended to represent a common tungsten filament light source and consists of a gas-filled incandescent lamp operating at 2854 K. CIE Source B consists of the Source A lamp with a special filter to approximate noon sunlight. CIE Source C employs the lamp of Source A with a special filter to approximate daylight (sunlight plus skylight).

Source C is in fact a very close approximation of natural daylight.

[1] Manager, Quality Assurance, Pulp and Paper Div., Kimberly-Clark Corp., Neenah, Wis.

Unfortunately the typical "daylight" fluorescent lamp is a poor approximation of natural daylight (Fig. 2). Since the visual appearance of a surface or object will vary as the spectral distribution of the illuminant is varied, it is desirable in making visual judgments of appearance that either: (1) the normal illuminant for the surface of object be matched or (2) judgments be made under three different illuminants (Source A or incandescent lamp, Source C or natural daylight, and a typical daylight fluorescent lamp).

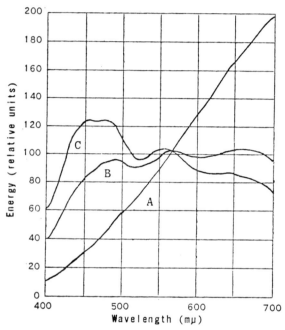

FIG. 1—*Relative energy distributions of CIE standard illuminants A, B, and C (Committee on Colorimetry), 1944c, p. 635).*

Although under certain conditions light may be visible between the wavelengths of 300 to 1000 millimicrons, the visible spectrum is normally considered to lie between the wavelengths of 380 and 770 millimicrons. As shown in Fig. 3, the sensitivity of the average observer's eye under photopic conditions (normal light levels) is greatest at a wavelength of about 555 millimicrons.

Intensity

In visual judgment of all appearance characteristics it is very important that the intensity of the illumination source be specified and controlled. In general, relatively high levels of illumination are preferred for maximum accuracy in visual judgments. It has been established that visual acuity, the ability to distinguish fineness of detail, increases as the illumination level increases, reaching a maximum at a level of approximately 1000 foot-candles. Contrast sensitivity also increases as the illumination level increases, and if the level falls below 10 foot-candles the luminance difference necessary for perception by the average eye increases markedly. Change in illumination intensity can also cause visual hue shifts, with

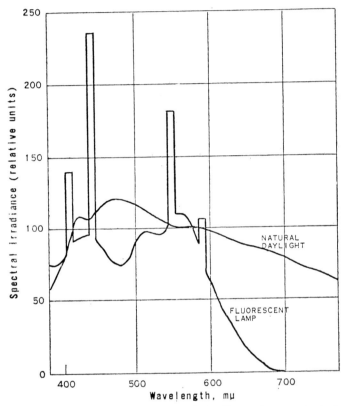

FIG. 2—*Relative distribution of spectral irradiance from a typical daylight fluorescent lamp (6500 K) as compared with that of natural daylight of about the same color (after Nickerson, 1962).*

increased illumination causing colors to become more yellow and blue, and less green and red. The influence of illumination level on color saturation is even more pronounced. As lumination intensity is increased above the chromatic threshold the visual saturation increases for all colors up to an optimum point, and then falls off with continued increase in intensity. The optimum point varies with wavelength, being least for purples and spectrum colors around 450 millimicrons, greatest for colors around 570 millimicrons, and again low around 650 millimicrons.

These effects of illumination intensity can be usefully employed in standardizing visual judgments in quality control and similar fields, where samples are being visually judged by different observers. It is possible to vary illumination intensity for each observer so that each one will have the same degree of visual acuity or contrast sensitivity as the

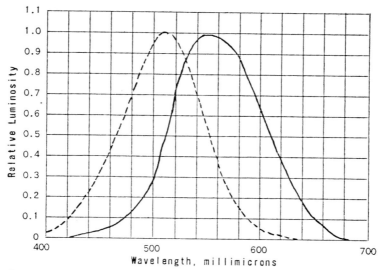

FIG. 3—*Scotopic luminating function (dashed line). Photopic curve is included for comparison. From Judd, D. B.,* Color in Business, Science and Industry, *Wiley, New York, 1952, Fig. 2, p. 9.*

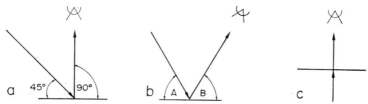

FIG. 4—*(a) Diffuse reflectance, (b) specular reflectance (A = B) and (c) transmitted light.*

other observers. This technique is particularly useful in quality control testing for nonuniformities in appearance, such as the detection and counting of flaws, dirt, or other nonuniformities in a product.

Viewing Conditions

Geometric Considerations

The angles of incidence of the illumination and of viewing of a surface or volume are of great importance in assessment of appearance. For each appearance characteristic and for each type of material there is an optimum relationship between these two angles. These fit into one of the three general types of geometries shown in Fig. 4.

1. *Diffuse reflectance*—Materials are illuminated at an angle of 45 deg and viewed at an angle of 90 deg to the surface, or they may be illuminated at 90 deg and viewed at 45 deg. This geometry, recommended by the CIE, is used for visual judgments of luminance and chromaticity, and for certain types of nonuniformities where contrast in luminance is the predominant factor (flaws, dirt specks, uniformity of printed matters, etc.).

2. *Specular reflectance*—The angle of incidence and of viewing are

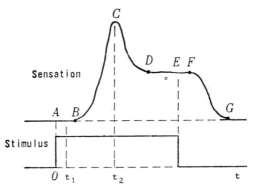

FIG. 5—*Diagram illustrating the course of the sensation resulting from a constant stimulus. Instead of beginning at A, at the same time as the stimulus, the sensation starts at B after a short delay (the latent period), then increases, passes through a maximum C, and subsequently falls again. Then the sensation (except for a stabilized image) remains more or less constant at the level DE. When the stimulus is removed suddenly, the sensation remains unchanged for a time, EF, and then disappears progressively from F to G. From LeGrand, Yves,* Light, Colour, and Vision, *(translated by Hunt, R. W. G., Walsh, J. W. T., and Hunt, F. R. W., Wiley, New York, 1957, p. 300.)*

equal. The best angle to use depends on the type of surface and must be determined experimentally. In general, rougher, low gloss surfaces are lighted and viewed at low angles. The sheen, or shine of textiles is best judged at very low (almost grazing) angles. Angles of this low magnitude are also usually best for visual judgments of textured and patterned surfaces. On the other hand, very smooth, high gloss surfaces are best judged visually at high angles of incidence and viewing.

3. *Transmitted light*—transparency and translucence are visually judged by degree of light transmission through a film or volume. The hiding power or opaqueness of a film may be visually evaluated by placing printed matter of varying blackness under the film, illuminating it from above, and determining the point at which the printed matter can be identified. In this special case the light is transmitted through the film,

reflected by the printed matter, and transmitted again through the film to the eye.

Viewing Time

A certain brief stimulation is required to permit any visual sensation to build up to maximum strength (Fig. 5). The duration of this interval varies with the individual and with the intensity of the stimulus, and varies between 0.1 and 0.3 s. If the visual judgment involves scanning of a surface or volume, such as would be the case during inspection of a moving web or of large sheets of material, and the viewing time for any area scanned is less than that required for maximum visual sensation, then the recognition of an appearance nonuniformity in the area will depend upon the "visual impact" of the nonuniformity. In such cases, if it is desired that only nonuniformities of a specific degree of "visual impact" be recognized, it is necessary that the viewing time per area of sample be specified and controlled. For example, in making visual counts of dirt specks in sheets of paper, where the specks may vary in size and blackness, the time allowed for inspection of each sheet must be standardized if agreement between observers is to be realized.

Sample Area and Juxtaposition

Spatial relationships within the visual field of the observer can affect appearance judgments. The angular size, or "visual angle," of a viewed area is the angle which the area subtends at the eye, regardless of the distance from the area to the eye. As the sample area increases:

1. Up to a certain angular size, the visual luminance of the sample increases.

2. Up to about 20 deg of visual angle, the visual color of the sample increases in degree of saturation.

3. Ability to detect differences in both luminance and chromaticity increases.

Whenever possible, areas to be compared or matched should be placed in juxtaposition. An observer's powers of discrimination are at a maximum when he is viewing two large adjacent areas with a sharp and almost invisible boundary line between them.

Background and Glare

The appearance of a surface or volume is influenced by the luminance and chromaticity of the immediately surrounding areas, particularly if there is a marked difference between these areas and the surface or volume being viewed. This effect is known as "contrast enhancement" and must be standardized if results obtained by different observers are to be in agreement. In general, dark backgrounds will make the subject look lighter, and light backgrounds will make it appear darker. Visual efficiency is at a maximum when the brightness of the central field is equal to that of the surroundings. In general, a brighter surrounding field reduces visual efficiency more than one which is darker than the central field. A medium neutral gray background is best for visual judgments of brightness and chromaticity.

"Glare" is caused by the presence in the field of view of some object which is either very bright compared with the general level of brightness to which the eye is adapted, or much brighter than the area being viewed. An unshaded lamp in the field of view is a typical example. Glare has two effects, both of which are undesirable. It will both reduce visual efficiency markedly (disability glare), and can cause unease, distraction, and fatigue (discomfort glare). For maximum visual efficiency it is to be avoided if at all possible.

Methods of Appearance Evaluation

Threshold Methods

Whether or not an appearance characteristic is visible depends upon the visual angle by which it is viewed, the degree of contrast present, its level of luminance, and the viewing time. Each of these factors must be equal to or greater than a certain threshold level, which in turn depends upon the levels of the other factors. Therefore, it may be possible to express the existing level of one factor in terms of the minimum level of another factor necessary for recognition of the appearance characteristic. For example, the degree of embossing of an embossed surface may be measured by gradually increasing the surface luminance by increasing the illumination level from zero to the point where the presence of embossing can be visually detected, holding visual angle, and viewing time constant. Or visual angle may be increased from a very small value to the point where the embossing can be detected, by reducing the distance between a fixed area of the surface and the eye, again holding the other factors constant. Degree of embossing can then be expressed, in the first case, in terms of illumination level necessary for perception, or, in the second case, in terms of the viewing distance necessary for perception.

Comparison Methods

The most common methods of visual judgment involve comparison of the test surface or volume with a standard of known value. Relatively permanent standards are established which represent different levels of an appearance characteristic, or may represent a single level of known desirability or undesirability. The test sample is visually compared with the standard or standards under fixed conditions of illumination and viewing and its relationship to the standard or standards determined. For the appearance attributes of color (lightness, hue, and saturation) a number of sets of established standards are available. Among the best known of these are the *Munsell Book of Color, The Container Corp. Color Harmony Manual,* the *Moerz and Paul Dictionary of Color,* and the *Villalobos Colour Atlas.*

Ranking Methods

Because of the remarkable sensitivity of the eye and the nondestructive nature of the visual judgment, it is possible to rank with accuracy large numbers of sample with regard to an appearance attribute. This method is of particular value in assessment of quality of printing, where the degree of non-uniformity in printed specimens is being considered. As many as 100 specimens can be ranked in a single array by a judge without excessive difficulty, if the fairly wide variations in printed appearance normally occurring in printability studies are present.

Numerical Counting Methods

It is possible to describe some appearance nonuniformities in terms of number of occurrences per stated quantity of surface or volume. For example, dirt specks in paper are often expressed in terms of number present per unit of surface area. The appearance of certain textile weaves may be described in terms of thread counts and diameters. The appearance of a printed specimen may be described in terms of the number of halftone dots missing in a stated printed area.